ABANDON ALL HOPE

A Postmodern Parable

PETER FENTON

D1600011

ORNITHOLOGY MEDIA

critical thought and laughter

This work is published by Ornithology Media, an imprint of
www.byPeterFenton.com

Copyright © 2021 by Peter Fenton

All rights reserved. No part of this publication may be
reproduced, stored or transmitted in any form or by any means,
electronic, mechanical, photocopying, recording, scanning, or
otherwise without written permission from the publisher. It is
illegal to copy this book, post it to a website, or distribute it by
any other means without permission.

Professionals and amateurs are hereby warned that this material,
being fully protected under the Copyright Laws of the United
States of America and all other countries of the Berne and
Universal Copyright Conventions, is subject to a royalty. All
rights including, but not limited to, professional, amateur,
recording, motion picture, recitation, lecturing, public reading,
radio and television broadcasting, and the rights of translation
into foreign languages are expressly reserved. To obtain
performance rights for this work, please visit
www.byPeterFenton.com

Second Edition

Edited by Kimberly Macasevich

ISBN: 978-1-7376182-5-6

TABLE OF CONTENTS

Melissa

—Libra/Scorpio/Sagittarius
—Self-appointed "savior" for homeless women in Pittsburgh
—Can't resist a selfie, even while drunk

Sean

—Game theory master
—Cocky, but usually right
—Lethal hazelnut allergy

Evan

—Preacher's kid
—Likes Chick—fil—A and "Biblical Gender Roles"
—Doesn't look both ways before crossing the street

Critical Acclaim for Abandon All Hope

"Sartre said, *'Hell is other people.'* Now imagine those other people are two nineteen-year-old college students who are absolutely sure they are right about everything and you're stuck with them in a dorm room for two for eternity. *Abandon All Hope* is funny as hell, and heavenly sweet. There's a message here that says it's best to accept what's good—and not so good—in ourselves and others, but it doesn't hit you over the head. And despite the title, there's a surprise ending that gives you reason to hope. A delightful read!"

—**Marjorie Bicknell,**
Dramatists Guild of America

"It put me right back in my dorm room.
What an adventure!"

—**Hank Chen,**
Actor

"What if Hell was a dorm room with two beds, two desks, and three people, with nothing to read but Paddington Bear erotica? *Abandon All Hope* runs with this idea in a playful upheaval of Christian heaven and hell mythology. The approach of satirizing good and evil is reminiscent of C.S. Lewis' *Screwtape Letters*, in which significant ethical questions are revealed through humor. *Abandon All Hope* is snort-out-loud funny. Can't wait to see it on stage and screen."

—Suzanne DeWitt Hall,
Author of *Where True Love Is* and *Sex With God*

"This play will stop you in your tracks and make you question, think, and evaluate your thinking and perspectives. *Abandon All Hope* allows the reader an opportunity to experience dark moments, yet there is a parallel track that leads you on a journey of empathy, reflection, and love. Just wow . . . this is not on a once-read and put away list. This is up for rereading."

—Jen Lowry,
Author of *The Sunday Killer*
Podcast Host of *Jen Lowry Writes*

"People torment themselves, God's a woman, and hell's a dorm room. This play nails it."

—J.E. Kraft,
Author of *The Survivors*

"I got pulled into the captivating story that Peter has written . . . The characters are all well developed and I think my only "complaint" was I didn't get to spend even more time getting to know these three. You see their strengths, passions, and vulnerabilities as fellow humans on life's journey."

—D. Gaines Taylor,
Founder of Refuge Faith Community

"The characters were so relatable. It was easy to get hooked into wanting to know what happened to them and if they indeed learned from their experience . . . I knew there would be a twist. You did not disappoint."

—Debbie Rodgers,
Executive Coach

"Thought-provoking, funny, and ultimately hopeful, this was a great little book that I really enjoyed . . . The characters are very well developed, each of them "good people" by their own standards but struggling with what that really means morally and theologically, and the plot is an intriguing one."

—Lillah Lawson,
Author and World Religions Expert

"*Abandon All Hope* is a brilliant play by Peter Fenton in which three newly deceased college freshmen find themselves in Hell. Their Hell comes in the form of a cramped college dorm room with only two beds among them. The three—a spunky feminist, an overly focused logistician, and an obnoxiously devout evangelical—embark on a diabolical contest at the hand of a wine-drinking demon to gain entrance into Heaven. The winner will immediately be transported to Heaven while the two remaining will be subjected to an eternity of suffering and torture. Will this contest truly have a winner?

As a lover of the theatre, I found the play captivating and thought-provoking. It is reminiscent of Sartre's *No Exit* but with a more contemporary take on the foibles of today's society. Is Hell a place or a state of mind each man creates for himself out of his own fears, prejudices, and insecurities? This provocative work of art will have you laughing while most importantly it will have you thinking and re-examining your own life. This is a play I'd very much love to see performed on stage . . . Peter Fenton has all the potential to make a significant mark on the theatrical world."

—Walter Roper,
Independent Book Reviewer

CAST OF CHARACTERS

When performed as a play, *Abandon All Hope* is written for a cast of four actors: two male, two female.

Actor #1: The Tormentor (F/35+/Any Ethnicity)
TERESA, a devilishly smirking "wine mom" type
PROF. AMY GONZALES (35+), a caring professor
SUE-ELLEN (35+), a woman in need
KRISTA (23-28), a charming scholar
JOYCE WEAVER (50s), a kind rural mom

Actor #2: The Humanist (F/18-25/Any Ethnicity)
MELISSA JONES, a scrappy femme fatale type
RACHEL (18-19), a morally conflicted girlfriend
DANNI (23-28), a bombastic radio host

Actor #3: The Rationalist (M/18-25/East Asian)
SEAN LIU-OGDEN, a wealthy valedictorian type
ISAIAH (18-19), a happy-go-lucky roommate
ANDREW TSUI (23-28), a sexy hedge fund manager

Actor #4: The Fundamentalist (M/18-25/Likely White)
EVAN DAIGLE, an eager "church camp counselor" type
JASON (23-28), a selfless protester
ADAM WEAVER (18-19), a playful dream boyfriend

Setting

The entirety of the play, save for the dream-like flashback sequences, takes place in Brimstone Hall, Room 664—an afterlife torture chamber that appears as a hellishly unkempt college dorm room in present-day Pennsylvania on an eerie October twilight. The room itself is pretty standard fare for an American dorm room in the 21st Century: there's two beds, two desks, and a bookshelf along the wall. On the wall are three pennants clustered together, one for each of Sean, Melissa, and Evan's universities (Ivy League, State, and Bible Colleges, respectively), and life-size portraits of Sean, Melissa, and Evan.

Chapter 3 takes place on the campus of Freedom University —a Bible College.

Chapter 5 takes place in and around a college town in Western Pennsylvania.

Chapter 7 takes place in Lancaster County, Pennsylvania in a suburban home and later at a fall fair.

INTRODUCTION

EACH ONE of us lives by some sort of code. Whether that code is religious, humanitarian, or scientific in nature, so many of us live believing our answer to the question "What really matters?" is both correct and universal. But at what point does clinging to your self-imposed beliefs begin to create Hell on Earth for you and those your life touches—and at what point will others abandon all hope in you?

At this moment in my life, I consider myself a former evangelical who's deconstructed and reconstructed my faith thoroughly enough to say with certainty that I believe there's a divine presence out there somewhere and I deeply love the teachings of Jesus. Personal beliefs regarding matters of faith have always proved hard to pin down with an organized religion label to capture all the nuance, but I've made a home in the Presbyterian Church USA. While I use Christian imagery and text throughout the play and *The*

Divine Comedy serves as a touchstone for Hell, I deliberately avoided claiming certainty on any specifics of theology or even in the existence of an afterlife in the story. I believe a person's ability to make the world a better or worse place operates independently of whether that person is part of an organized religion.

Looking back when I was nineteen, it's easy to see how I made life a living Hell for myself and those who loved me. I likely experienced some form of depression at that age. As I grew out of it and gained perspective (after two separate therapy journeys), I identified three core patterns of toxic behavior in my life. These patterns became the launching points for writing the roles of Evan, Sean, and Melissa. So where was I spending my time when I was nineteen years old, living out these journeys of self-discovery? I was in a college dorm room.

The whole experience of living in a college dorm as a commune of nineteen-year-olds is odd. For some, this adventure is the first real taste of sharing space with someone other than family and for all, life in the dormitory involves staying in extremely close quarters with people who live and think differently than you with nowhere to hide.

I arrived at college a wide-eyed evangelical freshman in 2013. As a youngest child with my own bedroom my entire life, I grew aware quickly that I had no place to retreat as I felt the every move and breath of my roommate, a stranger. Millions of questions about my roommates, my floormates, and myself swirled through my mind day in and day out:

- How am I coming across to all these new friends?
- Who will want to hang out with me today?
- When will my roommate stop playing *Super Smash Bros.* so I can sleep?
- What will these guys think if I share some otherwise hidden side of me?
- How are these people managing, by simply existing near me, to draw out my deepest insecurities?

It seemed only natural, then, for the torture chamber in my play to be modeled after a dorm room—a place that became, when I wasn't careful, my own personal circle of Hell.

Melissa Jones   Evan Daigle

Sean Liu

Top: Traber Hall, Room 618 at Wheaton College, 2013
Bottom: Peter Fenton outside Traber Hall, 2013

In the words of Oscar Hammerstein II, "Blossom of snow, may you bloom and grow—bloom and grow forever." *Abandon All Hope* is dedicated to you, dear reader. In as many ways as I feel the play is my personal manifesto wrestling with my relationships with existentialism, humanity, and organized religion disguised as comedy, I hope you take a look inside yourself to see what it is you're holding onto too tightly. I pray you stop contorting reality to fit a watered-down version that you are comfortable with and you continuously are open to learning how it is you build Heaven or Hell around you.

I also dedicate *Abandon All Hope* to the life and memory of Rachel Held Evans (1981-2019), whose own writing met countless at the gates of faith—touching the hearts, minds, and lives of both those looking for a way out and those looking for a way in.

I offer this humble story for the mantle of Rachel's legacy, as a face in the crowd who was touched by the life she lived.

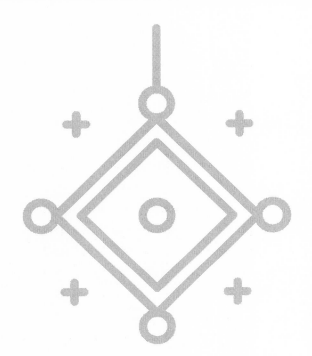

ACT ONE

CABERNET SAUVIGNON

Chapter One:
Red Wine

Act 1, Scene 1

BRIMSTONE HALL, *Room 664, on an eerie October twilight in the year 2019. The set is a lived-in (read: occupants are messy, male—hellishly unkempt) dorm room at an average state university in the United States. The furnishing is sparse: two beds, two desks, two chairs, and a bookshelf along the wall.*

White cinderblock wall encloses the room with a display of three pennants clustered together: Freedom University (a Bible college), Punxsutawney College of Pennsylvania (a State University), and Edgemere University (an Ivy League School). Three large portraits are hung on the wall displayed in another cluster, one respectively of EVAN (an eager "church camp counselor" type), MELISSA (a scrappy, femme fatale type), and SEAN (a wealthy valedictorian type). An open bottle of red wine stands next to an empty glass on one of the desks.

A glamorous "wine mom" type in a fiery red cocktail dress stands on a stepladder, hanging a wooden sign above the door—this is TERESA. She takes a step back to admire her work.

TERESA. *(Reading sign aloud.)* "Abandon all hope, ye who enter here"

EVAN. *(Offstage.)* I'm only saying this because I love you—

MELISSA. *(Offstage.)* I'm gonna need another vodka cider.

SEAN. *(Offstage.)* I'd do it. I'll be your hero.

Teresa smiles as she hears the echoes. She pours wine into the glass and takes a seat on top of the desk.

TERESA. It's a little bit on the nose, wouldn't you say, when they hang this big old sign above the entrance to Hell, the land of eternal damnation, telling you, "give up, it doesn't get better"? I'd imagine a human soul with an eternity of torture in front of them every moment of every day for the remainder of their existence would see this sign and think, "Yeah. No shit, Sherlock." Which means it's perfect.

Teresa sips her wine.

TERESA. I've hung it right there, above the door—maybe where a woman who looks like me would hang a "Live, Laugh, Love" sign from some cutesy hobby shop, but I'm no human woman. I'm a little tall—tall, dark, and gorgeous—but in the grand scheme of angels (or demons, for that matter) I'm pretty short and scrappy. That's why I've got these on.

Teresa indicates her shoes—a pair of pointy stilettos.

TERESA. Compensating for something. I know a few of you guys know what I'm talking about, huh? Yeah, thought so. I'm just so damn pleased with this sign. I plucked an idea right out of the myth of Hell—ya did good, Dante.

Teresa gets a closer look at the sign and notices it mistakenly reads:

Abandon all hoop,
ye who enter here.

TERESA. Ah, dammit. Get a look at this—ughhhh, man. How did I miss—?

Teresa sets her wine glass down and takes the sign off the wall.

TERESA. "Abandon all hoop, ye who enter—" Shit. I'm

about to trap humans in this room to look at a banner with a typo. At least the Comic Sans is torture enough. I have time though, I should fix—

Teresa grins.

TERESA. No! No. It would be just like Hell to know there's a typo on a sign and do nothing about it.

Teresa sets the sign back on the wall.

TERESA. But hey—since I've got time, why don't I give you a little tour? The door, of course, is only a prop—

Teresa opens the door, revealing more cinderblock wall.

TERESA. —just a tease. This room has "No Exit" because— well, you get it. It's barely big enough for one person. It's maybe bigger than, say, the broom closet you could rent in Manhattan for a thousand a month, but not by much. Two twin beds, two chairs, two desks—but no way to fully disappear into private studying or watching Netflix on a laptop. And definitely no privacy for porn.

Teresa picks up her wine glass and sits back on the desk.

TERESA. You might be thinking this is all pretty tame, especially if you've heard anything like I have about Hell. And I'd say you're right. This room is not designed for the very worst humanity has to offer, but it's perfect for my people. You have truly nowhere to hide from the roommate as you become increasingly aware of his every move and breath. Feeling a stranger's presence in such an intimate way when you didn't choose them—this might be torture in its purest form. You'll get to know their flaws like the back of your hand, and if you're paying enough attention, you'll become painfully aware of your own. If Jean-Paul Sartre was right when he said Hell is other people, then a freshman dorm room might just be your perfect picture of Hell on Earth.

Teresa takes a sip and looks around the room.

TERESA. Melissa Jones. Sean Liu. Evan Daigle. This'll torture all three of them. Oh yes, I've found the highest plane of torture by dormitory: three people sharing a room designed for two. Some universities actually do it on Earth, calling it a "forced triple," but whatever you call it, it's downright diabolical. Of course, most of these schools have the decency to put a third bed in the room—but that seemed a little too kind.

Teresa finishes the wine in her glass.

TERESA. It's almost time. I've got that kinda feeling in my stomach like I'm standing on a roof, looking over the edge and seeing the whole way down to the street—like if I stepped one toe out of line, I'd take a two-scream fall.

Teresa pours the rest of the bottle into her glass.

TERESA. You've heard of a two-screamer, right? When you're falling, screaming long enough that you have to take a breath and start a new scream before hitting the ground *(Laughs.)* You don't get to see those all the time, but that's how Melissa's about to die.

Teresa snaps her fingers. The lights go pitch black.

We hear a manic flurry of death scenarios playing out. The first thing we hear is a bus approaching.

RACHEL. *(Offstage.)* What are you doing? Evan, get out of the road!!

Guts splatter on the road as we hear the abrupt screech of a bus's brakes. At the same time, a woman is heard screaming—twice—shortly followed by a loud thud and a cracked skull.

13

ANDREW. *(Offstage.)* Oh my god!!

An ambulance is heard rushing to the scene as we hear severe allergic hyperventilating. A last gasp of life is given before the hyperventilating stops.

ADAM. *(Offstage.)* Sean??

A beat. Adam's heart splits in two.

ADAM. *(Offstage.)* Sean?

All sounds stop. We hang in the pitch black for just a moment while Teresa gets the last few details in order.

TERESA. *(In the dark.)* OK—that's perfect! So that's how it's all gonna go down. And the necklace goes right here. It's perfect. Let's get this party started.

Teresa snaps her fingers.

Chapter Two:
Strange Bedfellows

Act 1, Scene 2

BRIMSTONE HALL, *Room 664, continuous from the previous scene. Teresa's wine bottle, glass, and step-ladder have been cleared from the room. The lights go up and we see our three humans positioned around the room like propped-up corpses, blindfolded: EVAN at stage right, MELISSA at center stage, SEAN at stage left. Teresa grins at the audience.*

TERESA. Didn't mean to freak you out there—just had to get those final details strung together before bringing 'em in. So here's our people. Lively bunch, huh?

Teresa wanders among the three humans.

TERESA. Any coroner could tell you that death leaves little souvenirs on your body, your clothes, that tell your story—

and how that story ended. Vehicular manslaughter.
Traumatic brain injury. Anaphylactic shock.

Teresa continues to wander.

TERESA. So I like to keep my people stuck in the outfit
they wore on the last day. It's usually very telling. Melissa
spent what little money she had on whatever was in vogue—
this scarf was brand new and she was very happy to be seen
in it at her own birthday party. Sean was dressed for a
casual night out, but you just know he smells like money:
the jacket, the shoes, the watch. I think his underwear's
Armani—don't quote me on that. And Evan: wooden cross
necklace tucked under a Christian band graphic T and cargo
shorts. Would you believe he was the coolest kid in youth
group?

Teresa laughs.

TERESA. Fortunately, none of their stories are over.
They're frozen in a moment, experiencing nothing. Time is
standing still and each of them have no idea where they're
about to go—or that they're about to go anywhere. If I were
kinder maybe I'd let them stay like this, but we've got things
to do here.

Teresa removes Melissa's blindfold. Melissa comes to.

TERESA. Good evening, my queen!

Melissa is clearly confused. She looks around the room—it feels familiar, but something's obviously off. She can't quite place where she is.

TERESA. Welcome home. Sort of.

MELISSA. God, this is so embarrassing. I must've blacked out, 'cause I can't remember a damn thing. Those vodka ciders—wait. This isn't my room. Who are you? Did we—? Why's my picture here?

Melissa crosses to the photo of herself.

MELISSA. Ugh, this is an awful picture. Why would anyone hang this?

TERESA. Loved your feed, girl!

MELISSA. All my selfies and that's the one you go with?

TERESA. All your selfies and that's the one I went with. It

just stuck out to me. Don't know what to tell ya, just had a certain . . . palpable hollowness to it. Felt like it just screamed "You!"—hashtag resist!

MELISSA. Okay, I have no idea who you are or how I got here, but I need to get back to my party—

Melissa opens the door, revealing more cinderblock wall.

MELISSA. What the—what?

TERESA. Look, I don't want to give the orientation spiel three times. Just hang tight, I'm gonna wake the others.

MELISSA. Hang on. Is this a kidnapping??

TERESA. You're not wrong—but that's maybe the harshest way to describe what I do. But how would you possibly get that idea?

MELISSA. Well clearly you've been stalking me or something—my picture's up on the wall, you know I settled for Punxsutawney but I wanted to go to Edgemere so badly —

Melissa notices the third pennant on the wall.

MELISSA. But what's Freedom University? Ew, is that some kind of Republican—?

Teresa removes Sean's blindfold. Sean comes to.

TERESA. Sean—

MELISSA. Whoa, where the hell did he come from?

SEAN. *(Without missing a beat.)* Atlanta.

TERESA. Sean—buddy. I'm so glad you're here.

Melissa checks Sean out.

MELISSA. Me too.

TERESA. Yeah, good luck with that. Sean, I'm curious if you heard—any of that. Does 'Black-Bottom Hazelnut Pie' mean anything to you?

Sean looks on, blank.

SEAN. I'm allergic to hazelnuts.

TERESA. How about 'The Great American Dumpster-Fire'?

SEAN. No. I've never been to New Jersey.

TERESA. Not ringing any bells?

SEAN. I have genuinely no idea what you're talking about.

TERESA. Interesting. Very interesting . . .

Teresa removes Evan's blindfold. Evan comes to.

MELISSA. Okay seriously, I want answers right now. Who are you? Why have you kidnapped us? Why is there a terrible picture of me on the wall?

Evan and Sean look over at Melissa's photo on the wall. Sean notices his own photo—which is his acting headshot. He rolls his eyes.

MELISSA. What the hell is going on here?

TERESA. Funny choice of words there, Missy.

MELISSA. Excuse me?

TERESA. What you said. I found it funny.

MELISSA. I'm asking you questions that any decent person would answer, don't you dare patronize me like—

TERESA. Anyone ever tell you how cute you get when you're angry?

MELISSA. This is injustice, if you think you can keep dodging—

TERESA. Hell. Hell is what's going on here. That's why I thought it was cute. All three of you: you died. You're in Hell.

A beat.

TERESA. Welcome!

MELISSA. No, no. No. Cut the bullshit, what's really going on here?

TERESA. You're dead. This is the start of your afterlife and I'm telling you now: You're in Hell. Evan was hit by a bus. Melissa fell off a roof. Sean choked on pie. You each died at a similar quality of soul at age nineteen in the state of Pennsylvania on the night of Friday, October 11th. You each have a very good reason you're here. No bullshit. And per the regulations as handed down from God and Jesus up in corporate, you three have been assigned to my care!

MELISSA. So . . . is this how it goes? You tell us we're in Hell and just expect us to believe religion is real now, all of a sudden? And what, I guess that makes you Satan?

Evan bristles. Teresa laughs.

TERESA. You think *Satan himself* has time in his schedule to torture you? You?!? Nah. Call me Teresa. Or Momma T!

EVAN. Are you a demon?

TERESA. Yeah, let's go with that. For your sake right now —I'm a demon. I prefer "Guardian," but sure. Don't look at me like I'm some kind of monster, though. I'm more like your fun aunt! And look who's finally awake! How ya doing, Evan?

EVAN. Hi.

TERESA. So, this is Brimstone Hall, Room 664.

MELISSA. What, Room 666 was already taken?

TERESA. As a matter of fact, yes! That's the room right next door. It's Josef, Benny, and—ah, what was his name?

Through the walls, we hear an angry male voice shouting in German. Teresa grins.

TERESA. Oh! Adolf. Duh. So the three of you are confined to this room, forever. I'll be in and out to torture, but I'm pretty confident you won't need any help from me.

Teresa cackles as she gestures to sign.

EVAN. "Abandon all hope, ye who enter here."

MELISSA. That font was a choice.

SEAN. There's a typo on that sign. It says hoop, not hope.

MELISSA. "Abandon all hoo—." So what? Who cares?

SEAN. I do. It's not the way it should be. "Abandon all *hope*, ye who enter here" means something. "Abandon all hoop" means nothing. You're going to fix that, right?

TERESA. No.

EVAN. B-but wait a second. There must be some mistake. I don't belong in Hell.

TERESA. Nah. You do.

EVAN. This- this can't be Hell.

TERESA. It always takes a minute. But trust me: you'll come around to it. You'll accept your fate.

EVAN. No. I don't accept this.

TERESA. Mmmm—the plot thickens.

EVAN. I'd do anything to get into Heaven. Anything.

TERESA. Anything, huh? Why don't I hold you to it? *(Laughs.)* You see, I've hidden something of great power in this room. Before a demon is given her first batch of humans to torture, she's given a talisman. *(Clarifying.)* A magical necklace—it's a lot of fun! It gives her the power to do some of the more spectacular torture.

SEAN. Define spectacular.

TERESA. Any nightmare your little heart can dream up. I

love simulating childbirth—lotta men crumble when I do
that one to them. I'd show ya if I had it with me!! All you
have to do is put the talisman around your neck,
concentrate, bring forth all the powers of Hell, and you just
—make it happen! Without it, I mean—my powers are like a
step above a birthday party magician.

SEAN. So essentially: you hid a talisman somewhere in this
room, and you want us to find it because without it you
can't really torture us because you're basically a birthday
clown? I don't understand the incentive here—

TERESA. Find the talisman in this room anytime starting
tomorrow morning and present it to me. I'll get you right
into Heaven. I've got some contacts up there from when I
was on shoulder duty—I'll slide you in and the powers that
be will be never-the-wiser.

EVAN. Oh my gosh, that's amazing! We gotta find this
thing.

SEAN. But why bother with the game if you're planning to
take us to Heaven? Seems counterproductive unless you're
some kind of rogue demon or—

TERESA. Well here's the catch: I'm only saving one of you.

Only one of you can find the talisman and be saved. The other two will be stuck in this room forever—and I'll be reunited with my talisman. Operating at full power. You see, Mr. Know-It-All, the numbers speak for themselves. You don't grace the top twenty-five on the leaderboard without some kind of outside-the-box strategy.

Teresa cackles.

TERESA. One of you will find it. Tomorrow morning, it's game on. In the meantime—have fun getting to know each other!!

Teresa exits. Evan retreats into a corner and prays.

MELISSA. Where did she—?

Melissa opens the door again.

MELISSA. Oh. Right. Did she just—vanish? What was her name? (*Shouts.*) Denise?! (*To herself.*) Looked like a fucking Denise.

SEAN. Teresa.

Act 1, Scene 3

Brimstone Hall, Room 664, continuous from the previous scene. Evan prays, desperately, in a corner as Melissa paces the floor in utter shock regarding the sheer amount of information she has just been given. Sean looks on both, not losing any composure for such a silly matter as learning he's arrived in Hell.

MELISSA. Okay. Okay, deep breaths. *(Exhales.)* Okay. This is probably all a dream. Pinch me.

SEAN. What?

MELISSA. Pinch me. I'll wake up and this will all be over.

SEAN. Uh, no. Pretty sure we're dead. And this is the afterlife.

MELISSA. Well, no. This bizarro dorm room isn't the afterlife. There's no such thing.

SEAN. Says who?

MELISSA. Science.

SEAN. *(Laughs.)* Well, I'm a scientist. While many if not most scientists would take an agnostic posture toward the possibility of, say an afterlife or even the existence of a god, there is no field of study or body of scientists, even metaphysicists, that would completely exclude the possibility of —

MELISSA. Huh?

SEAN. Are you not following me? I dumbed it down for you.

MELISSA. No—I. Maybe we got off on the wrong foot. I'm Melissa Jones. Pronouns she/her. Sophomore poli-sci major at Punxsutawney. Delta Zeta. I'm an intersectional feminist —I advocate for all people.

SEAN. My name's Sean. I—

MELISSA. I devoted my life to fighting for justice. I came from nothing. My mom's a hairdresser in South Philly and I never met my dad. I see strong women like my mom and my sister and I want to—walk alongside them as someone who's been there before. Invest in the marginalized worldwide. Use my words and my platform to inspire people to change the world. I'll run for Congress the minute I turn twenty-five.

SEAN. Okay, wow. Sounds like you're—one of a kind.

MELISSA. Oh, thanks!

SEAN. My name's Sean. I go to Edgemere -

MELISSA. Of course you do. Geez. I really should've gone there. That school was just way too expensive.

SEAN. It's an Ivy, what do you expect? Anyway—I'm a freshman engineering major. Sophomore by credit, actually. I took a gap year in the Alps after graduating. My mom said it would be good for my soul, or whatever. I'll probably finish undergrad in two and a half years *(Laughs.)* Well— maybe not anymore, since I'm dead.

MELISSA. I feel like I've seen you before. Like—do I know you? Do we all somehow know each other?

SEAN. I don't think I'd trust your judgment enough to say if you'd seen me before.

Evan finishes his prayer. He gets up and turns to face Melissa and Sean.

MELISSA. Well. Whatever. I know I've seen you . . . I just can't place where. *(Turns to Evan.)* What about you? You've been awfully quiet.

EVAN. I'm having trouble understanding why . . . why I'm here.

MELISSA. That's valid. I saw you praying—are you religious?

EVAN. I wouldn't say that I'm a religious person, but I have a personal relationship with Jesus Christ.

MELISSA. So . . . super religious.

EVAN. Christianity is not a religion, it's a relationship.

SEAN. You can't be serious. It's not a relationship. It's a religion.

EVAN. How would you know? It's not like you're a believer.

SEAN. And how do you know that?

EVAN. Well, I'm a Christian. Only Christians go to Heaven, so people who go to Hell are not. You're probably not a

Christian.

SEAN. By your own logic, though, that only tells me that *you're* not a Christian. Which I doubt is true, since you claim to have a personal relationship with Jesus Christ. Let's say for the sake of the argument, I'm also a Christian.

EVAN. Are you?

SEAN. Let's suppose I am. Given that you say you're a Christian and I say that I'm a Christian, it's a self-applied label on both ends, beholden to whatever our individual interpretations as to what it means to be a Christian. Since we're both using the same label to describe ourselves, this therefore renders the label "Christian" in and of itself— meaningless.

EVAN. You're saying being a Christian is . . . meaningless?

SEAN. No, not at all. There's just no way of quantifying, say, you're "more" Christian than me because with self-applied labels like *Christian* or *righteous* or *sexy*, it just means whatever the person wants it to mean.

EVAN. But you'd know. You'd just know if you believe— like, really believe. Jesus Christ is my lord and savior and

He fights for me. He's my everything. "When the world tells you no way—you tell 'em Yahweh." I think of being a Christian this way: if you were put on trial for following Jesus, would there be enough evidence to convict you?

SEAN. That's not a very good argument. The first thing the hypothetical jury would look for is where you spent your time. I went to Catholic school K through 12, straight-A student and all the nuns loved me, I go to mass with my parents whenever we're all in the same place on any given Sunday—

EVAN. Going to church doesn't make you a Christian any more than standing in a garage makes you a car.

Sean and Melissa stare at Evan, blank.

MELISSA. Oh boy. I forgot how much religion just poisons people—

EVAN. I can't even begin to tell you how wrong you are and how much Jesus loves you.

MELISSA. Think about how much evil is done in the name of religion: Crusades. Touchy priests. Those weird white savior mission trips to Africa. And you train little girls to be housewives from birth like it's been 1958 for sixty years—

SEAN. Technically sixty-one years.

MELISSA. And don't even get me started on a woman's right to choose—

EVAN. My mom loves being a stay-at-home mom. It was her right to choose being at home, raising three sons.

MELISSA. Well. Good for her.

EVAN. What even gives you life or hope? Since you're not a Christian?

MELISSA. Look. Humanity has evolved past any primitive need for religion. Just do the right thing when you can, it's really that easy.

EVAN. How do you know right from wrong if you don't believe in God?

MELISSA. You just—do? Nobody needs a wizard overlord to tell them that killing people is bad. And if you do—that tells me literally everything I need to know about you.

EVAN. It sounds like you had something hard happen in your life. And you grew to blame God for it.

MELISSA. Incorrect. I believe there is no god.

EVAN. How can you hate something you don't believe exists?

MELISSA. Exactly. I can't hate God, since I believe he does not exist. It might do you some good to open your eyes first and then maybe a science book. I need real evidence if I'm going to believe in anything.

SEAN. Don't pretend there's no evidence for God. The problem for me is the evidence we have may be necessary but it's certainly not sufficient.

MELISSA. Come on, seriously? Whose side are you on?

SEAN. I'm on no one's side. Given we can trust the demon to some extent, she says she got regulations from God in corporate. Any argument for the non-existence of God could completely fall apart if this new evidence could be corroborated—

MELISSA. Oh, shut up.

Act 1, Scene 4

Brimstone Hall, Room 664, a couple hours later. Night has fallen. Sean, Melissa, and Evan sit on the floor in a circle—they've been playing a joyless card game (a joyless card game—for everyone but Sean, that is) for some amount of time. Sean lays a card in the middle.

SEAN. And that's game!! Made my bet this round. So, for final scores, we have . . . I win with one hundred forty-seven points, Melissa comes in second with eighty-four, and Evan is—

EVAN. Dead last.

SEAN. Accurate. You're dead and you came in last. Another round?

MELISSA. Unless we're playing strip poker, not interested.

Sean picks up all the cards and puts them back in a box. Melissa yawns. Sean looks Evan in the eye.

SEAN. What's wrong, man?

EVAN. It's weird. I shouldn't be in Hell. I don't belong here.

SEAN. It, uh, looks like this room was set up for you. There's your picture—and I assume you go to Freedom University?

EVAN. Yep. Bible-believing Christian college in central Pennsylvania. Our President Jeremy Fallow Jr. is on the National Religious Liberty Task Force for President Tr—

SEAN. *(Snippy, with contempt.)* I'm familiar.

MELISSA. Christians. Always saying shit like, "Heaven or Hell? Do you know where you're going when you die?" I gotta say, this is some unbelievable karmic justice that you're here with the nonbelievers in Hell. Makes me feel a little better that the universe is on the right side of this one.

Melissa crosses to bed.

MELISSA. All right, good night.

SEAN. Wait—there's only two beds. How are we—? Someone's gotta double up—

EVAN. No. We can't—that's—

MELISSA. What's the big deal? Never shared a bed before?

EVAN. No, of course not. I've always thought the only woman I'd ever share a bed with would be my wife.

MELISSA. Your w—how old are you?

SEAN. *(To Evan.)* So just share with me. Why not?

EVAN. No! I—that's. No.

SEAN. So . . . OK, then. Let's draw lots to see who gets to sleep where. Two lots for each bed and—I don't know, maybe one lot if you draw it you have to sleep on the floor. It's the only fair and objective thing. *(Pause.)* Uh—what can we use for lots?

MELISSA. Who said anything about this being fair?? I'm not sleeping on the floor. That's a hard no. And I would prefer to share a bed, actually. And—come on. *(Turns to Sean.)* My decision of *who* would be pretty easy.

SEAN. I think that would be weird. For Evan. I'd rather not.

MELISSA. Oh, come on! Read the room, Sean—

SEAN. *(Laughs.)* What, you have a crush on me?

MELISSA. No, it's just—given the two options—

SEAN. Well. The feeling isn't mutual. I'm just going to make the executive call that we draw lots. What can I grab here?

EVAN. No. We don't have to.

SEAN. Uh . . . why not?

EVAN. I can sleep on the floor. Nobody has to share a bed.

SEAN. Really?

EVAN. Yeah. It's what Jesus would do.

MELISSA. Would he?

EVAN. Yeah. I think He would. He sacrificed everything, I think I can sacrifice a night in a bed.

MELISSA. Good old Christian martyrdom. No complaints here.

Melissa collapses into bed and promptly falls asleep.

SEAN. You sure you don't want to share with me?

EVAN. No thanks. I'm good.

SEAN. OK.

Evan turns out the overhead light and lies down on the floor. Seeing this, Sean picks up one of the pillows from his bed and crosses to Evan.

SEAN. For your head. (*A beat.*) Obviously.

Evan takes the pillow. Sean—a little embarrassed—scurries back to his bed, climbs in, and falls asleep.

EVAN. Thanks.

Evan sets the pillow on the floor and lies down.

EVAN. (*To himself.*) It's what Jesus would do.

This is a eureka moment for Evan—he sits straight up.

EVAN. I just did what Jesus would do. (*Calls out.*) Teresa!

Teresa enters.

TERESA. Ah! I was hoping one of you would call me in!

EVAN. I need to speak with God.

TERESA. Oh yeah? What do you wanna tell Her Holiness?

EVAN. "Her"—?

TERESA. God's not dead and God is a girl! Isn't that fun?

EVAN. I guess so.

TERESA. You won't be able to see God tonight, but your concern is very important to Her, you can just tell me! What would you want to say to God right now?

EVAN. I don't belong here.

TERESA. Nope. You do. Sorry, sweetheart. *Thus saith the Lord.* She's incapable of being wrong. Or do you not believe your God is perfect?

EVAN. I do believe God is perfect—but something's wrong. I should not be here.

TERESA. And why would you think that?

EVAN. Just now, as we were all deciding who would sleep where—I offered to sleep on the floor. It's a small thing, but I did it without thinking. It didn't even cross my mind that it's what Jesus would do but I just—did it. Maybe it was just years of building a life imitating Christ. I gave my life to Him and spent every moment working to spread the Gospel. I only read the Bible-believing authors like Ragsdale—

TERESA. Ah, yes. *The Battle for Manhood*, Dean Ragsdale.

EVAN. I wasn't a macho bro or anything, but I was a strong Biblical man—a quest to endure, a war to win, and a princess to save. That was me, that was all I wanted in life. I believed all the right things and Jesus said *whosoever believeth* will inherit eternal life.

TERESA. And this . . . isn't eternal life?

EVAN. No. I lived in such a way as to guarantee that one day I would be back face-to-face with God Himself.

TERESA. Herself.

EVAN. If you're saying that God is real and H . . . "She" made everything and Jesus died to save us if we only believe, I see no good reason why I'm in Hell.

TERESA. I feel for ya, hon. I really do. But there's a really good reason you're here, Evan Daigle, and honestly if you can't tell already—

EVAN. I just—I don't get it.

TERESA. Take a moment. Strip away thinking, *"I'm a Christian,"* and just look at the things you do, the way you treat people—

EVAN. But everything I do is because I'm a Christian. You can't do something about any of this? Bend the rules for a sinner saved by grace, like me?

A grin spreads across Teresa's face.

TERESA. How about I show you how you died? This could be interesting. This is gonna blow your mind . . . You got hit by a bus!

EVAN. Whoa—I don't remember that at all.

TERESA. What do you last remember?

EVAN. I . . . It's weird—so . . . foggy. Everything that day.

TERESA. Yeah, let's jog your memory . . . Close your eyes. Here's your cautionary Bible story.

EVAN. My what?

TERESA. Just close your eyes . . .

Evan closes his eyes. Teresa wraps a blindfold around him and ties it.

CHAPTER THREE:
THE BIBLE CLEARLY SAYS

The Cautionary Paralle of
Evan Daigle

The following chapter chronicles Evan's memory of his final day on Earth. Contemporary Christian Rock music plays in the background. Evan visualizes Teresa as PROF. AMY GONZALES, Sean as ISAIAH, and Melissa as RACHEL.

Act 1, Scene 5

PROFESSOR AMY *Gonzales' office in the Communications Department at Freedom University, early afternoon on Friday, October 11th. Evan stands at the open door frame. AMY sits in an office chair, facing away from Evan. Evan knocks on the door.*

EVAN. Professor Gonzales?

Amy turns around in the office chair to face Evan.

AMY. So! Tell me about your project, Evan. What's going on?

EVAN. I'm happy with it so far. My speech is all ready to go, just working on the PowerPoint.

AMY. Oh! That's—well—I wanted to meet one-on-one because I wanted to understand what you were getting at. Or maybe help you choose a new topic.

EVAN. W-what? Why?

AMY. So your assignment is an extemporaneous speech laying out two opposing arguments on a controversial topic without giving away which side you favor. And you've submitted a proposal in which you will give a speech laying out arguments regarding . . . "male friendship and masculinity."

EVAN. Yes. It's something I'm very passionate about and needs to be reclaimed in my generation.

AMY. So tell me about it. I don't quite understand.

EVAN. I wouldn't expect you to, since you're . . .

AMY. And neither did Peter, my TA.

EVAN. Part of becoming a strong man of God is . . . uh,

being in relationship. Learning how to express . . . feelings. Friendship. I think guys are told that Biblical manhood means you have to be tough, but . . . everyone's different. Some guys aren't macho, but that doesn't make us any less men of God. That shouldn't be held against us, because we are all the same at our core. Ragsdale says, "Inside the soul of every man are three unshakable desires: a quest to endure, a war to win, and a princess to save."

AMY. . . . OK. Sounds like you've read *a* book.

EVAN. But society today is failing us. I read a study where 20% of men say they have no friends. And when you think about how many more men commit suicide than women—

AMY. That is very sad to hear. But I don't understand how this relates to the assignment—where are the multifaceted arguments you can draw out?

EVAN. Uh—well, a lot of *feminists* or . . . "the gays" would argue that men don't matter.

Amy raises an eyebrow—confused.

EVAN. Well—society has made these parades for people

defying Biblical lifestyles and they think men shouldn't be celebrated for . . . being God-honoring men. When is straight pride month? Where are the people protesting for men's rights?

AMY. Hmm. There's this concept I think would blow your mind called Standpoint Theory. It could give you a whole new way to approach conversations about gender and you could even apply its principles when thinking about race, class, sexuality—

Amy notices Evan's face washing over.

AMY. But that's a lesson for a different day. You are clearly passionate about what you believe in and I do admire that. Sorry, Evan, but this topic, unfortunately, is a presentation for nobody. (*A beat.*) So let's think about some real controversies you could present on—

Act 1, Scene 6

Remington Hall, Room 207 (Evan's dorm room) at Freedom University, later that afternoon on Friday, October 11th. His roommate, ISAIAH, sits on his bed with an acoustic guitar in hand, strumming and picking away. Evan enters.

ISAIAH. Yo! What's wrong, man?

EVAN. Gonzo. She rejected my topic. We talked for like an hour and I have to start the whole thing over again.

ISAIAH. Oh, dude! That sucks.

EVAN. Yeah. She wants me to come back later today when I've written a new proposal. We got talking a lot about gender roles . . . might make my speech about whether women should preach.

ISAIAH. Wait, what's the controversy there?

EVAN. I don't think there is any. The Bible's pretty clear: "Wives, submit to your husbands." "A woman should remain silent in church." "I do not permit a woman to teach over a man."

ISAIAH. So is that going to be hard? To look unbiased?

EVAN. Yeah, definitely.

ISAIAH. Would it be better to . . . just preach the Truth?

EVAN. Normally, yeah. But I won't. Gonzo's the one

grading this project, so I gotta please her. And if I nail this, I get an A in Public Speaking. *(A beat.)* But she did say something weird. Like . . . there's some kind of theory she wants me to learn—that will blow my mind about, uh, gender and sex.

ISAIAH. That doesn't sound Biblical.

EVAN. No.

ISAIAH. Anyway! Can I show you this song I've been working on? It's a mashup of the hymn, "This is My Father's World" with "Colors of the Wind" from *Pocahontas*—

EVAN. I wonder if Gonzo's saved.

ISAIAH. Of course she is. Doesn't everyone have to sign the statement of faith at Freedom?

EVAN. They do. But how hard is it to sign something you don't believe? To be a false teacher operating in the name of God?

ISAIAH. People would . . . do that?

EVAN. The Enemy would. "Beware false teachers"—

ISAIAH. Whoa. I didn't even think about that.

EVAN. Lookin' out for you, bud.

Act 1, Scene 7

The sidewalk next to a busy street on the campus of Freedom University on the evening of Friday, October 11th. Evan enters, walking hand in hand with his girlfriend, RACHEL. Basically, Rachel held Evan's hand from freshman orientation week until this particular moment on October 11th. Evan was safe and sweet —which was enough for a nervous Rachel to let him pursue her. Evan tries to kiss Rachel. She steps away and squeezes his hand.

EVAN. I really wish Gonzales would just let me do my first idea. I don't want to have to research women preaching. Goes against God's design.

RACHEL. I think it'll be good for you. When was the last time you read something you didn't agree with? To at least try to understand?

EVAN. What, you do that?

RACHEL. Well, I read Ragsdale, and I don't really agree with him—at all.

EVAN. What?

RACHEL. But—I wanted to see where you were coming from, since I care about you.

EVAN. I—you told me you loved it.

RACHEL. I said it was really interesting.

EVAN. Yeah—really interesting. You enjoyed it.

RACHEL. I enjoyed understanding your perspective better. It was interesting to me how medieval he is. Just . . . like, super old-fashioned!

EVAN. The Truth of the Gospel doesn't go out of fashion.

RACHEL. Evan, *The Battle for Manhood* isn't a book of the Bible. You can't seriously look me in the eye and tell me I'm some princess that needs to be saved.

EVAN. It's only a metaphor.

RACHEL. Yeah, but it's a pretty sexist metaphor—and come on. There's no part of me that wants to be some submissive housewife or—

EVAN. Jesus can change any heart.

RACHEL. Oh—oh God, I wasn't planning to have this conversation with you yet.

EVAN. What?

RACHEL. I—I think we need a break. I don't think this is going to work . . . you and me.

EVAN. Why?

RACHEL. I thought maybe I could change, or you could change —I kept praying over and over that I could be a good girlfriend for you.

EVAN. You're the perfect girlfriend. I prayed for one and God gave me you.

RACHEL. I . . . it really just feels like I'm using you.

EVAN. That's how the world dates. But as Christians, we're

preparing for marriage.

RACHEL. No—Evan. I don't think I could marry you. That's the point.

A beat.

RACHEL. I've been coming to terms realizing—I—I like girls. Maybe also guys. I—I really, uh—if I look back on certain people . . . and feelings I've felt that were more than friendship . . . I know I've fallen for women before. And when I think about how desperately you want me—I've tried to get there, Evan. I could list out all these reasons why I should find you attractive . . . but . . . it's not fair. It's not fair for you to keep—

Rachel trails off as she tries to find an eloquent thought. She frustratedly blurts out:

RACHEL. Evan, I'm bi. Or gay. Maybe. I don't know.

Silence. Evan whips out a Bible.

EVAN. Have you even read this?

RACHEL. Yes—of course I have—

EVAN. I'm only saying this because I love you, but the Bible clearly says the gays are going to Hell.

RACHEL. *(Laughs; uncomfortable.)* Weird way to say "I love you" for the first time—

Evan opens the Bible and flips to a verse. Rachel realizes this is serious.

EVAN. Romans One. "God gave them over to shameful lusts. *Even their women* exchanged natural sexual relations for unnatural ones. In the same way, the men also abandoned natural relations with women and were inflamed with lust for one another."

RACHEL. I think it's a little more nuanced than just spewing Bible verses out of—

EVAN. The wages of sin is death. God said it, I believe it—that settles it!

Evan steps out into the street.

EVAN. Genesis Eighteen. "Then the Lord said, 'Because the outcry against Sodom and Gomorrah is great and their sin is very grave—'"

In the distance, we hear a bus approaching—and there's no chance of it slowing down.

RACHEL. What are you doing? Evan, get out of the road!!

EVAN. No!! I will stand here until you renounce the sin of homosexuality. Begone, demon! In the name of Jesus Christ —

RACHEL. Watch out!!

Evan disappears. Guts splatter on the road as we hear the abrupt screech of a bus's brakes. Rachel covers her mouth, shocked and horrified.

CHAPTER FOUR:
SECOND MOUSE GETS
THE CHEESE

Act 1, Scene 8

BRIMSTONE HALL, *Room 664, continuous from before Evan's flashback. Sean and Melissa are asleep in the two twin beds. Teresa stands next to Evan. Evan removes the blindfold.*

EVAN. Whoa.

TERESA. Yeah.

EVAN. My last words were "Jesus Christ." That's pretty amazing.

Evan lays down and drifts off.

TERESA. Is that really what you should take away from . . . any of that?

EVAN. *(Mumbled.)* Nothing on my breath but Jesus Christ.

Teresa smiles to herself as Evan drifts off to sleep. Teresa exits.

Act 1, Scene 9

Brimstone Hall, Room 664, the next morning. Evan is lying on the floor, Sean and Melissa each occupy one of the two beds. Evan gets up. He starts tearing the room apart, looking for the talisman. Sean gets up. He crosses to the desk and sits down.

EVAN. Come on, come on, come on, come on. Lord— where are you?

Sean pulls out a pen and paper. He writes out strategies. Evan turns to see him.

EVAN. What are you doing?

SEAN. Game theory scenarios.

EVAN. What game?

SEAN. This one. Looking for Teresa's talisman. It's all a game. I've been thinking about this all night, analyzing what

I know about you and Melissa and Teresa, and unless our variables change, it's going to be the dominant strategy for me to hang back initially.

EVAN. Cool. So—I guess *I'll* be the one finding it.

SEAN. No. I'm very much planning to win. And I will. I'll leave these notes behind as a souvenir if you ever want to see how I broke the game. I just have to position myself to benefit from the mistakes of everyone else. So, go—keep looking for the thing. You're behaving exactly how I need you to.

EVAN. Wait—you're studying me?

SEAN. Only for the purposes of winning. I expect this to be an "early bird gets the worm, but the second mouse gets the cheese" kind of deal. Maybe I've said too much. Carry on.

EVAN. I—

SEAN. Don't be intimidated. I like you. I want to be friends.

EVAN. Thanks. I guess.

SEAN. Yeah. For sure.

Evan resumes tearing the room apart. Sean briefly wonders why he said that before he resumes writing. Melissa turns awake. She sits up in bed.

MELISSA. Morning, boys. I have an idea.

SEAN. *(Not looking up.)* I'm way ahead of you.

MELISSA. So I see. Can you maybe stop for a moment? Both of you?

Sean and Evan stop to look at Melissa. Melissa gets up from the bed.

MELISSA. My woman's intuition is telling me that the demon's lying.

EVAN. About what?

MELISSA. I don't know. Gut feel—I really don't trust her.

SEAN. So . . . that's it? That's your idea?

MELISSA. Let me finish. Let's refuse to compete. We find the necklace together. If anything she said about it is true, we can figure out a way to use her own necklace to destroy her. Turn her into confetti or whatever.

EVAN. But then . . . we don't go to Heaven.

MELISSA. Yeah, but what if that isn't even a real option? Me, I wouldn't mind spending eternity in a boring room if it meant—I mean, if we do this right, we get to overthrow a dictator! Come on, I lived for this shit!

Sean looks Melissa in the eyes.

SEAN. I think that's a terrible idea.

MELISSA. Okay—I've definitely seen you before. Are you famous or something?

SEAN. God, you're still stuck on that?

EVAN. Don't you get it? We don't go to Heaven unless one of us gives her the necklace. Call me crazy, but I think we can trust her. She doesn't seem all that bad. Actually—almost seems like she's looking out for us.

MELISSA. She's basically the devil! Didn't they teach you about not making a deal with the devil in Sunday School? Or were you not paying attention that day?

EVAN. We didn't talk about the devil that much.

MELISSA. And even if everything she told us is true and you win, you'll spend eternity knowing the only reason you're in Heaven is because a demon was nice to you. How could you live with that?

SEAN. Well, technically, we're all dead—

MELISSA. Shut up.

EVAN. Even the shadow of a chance to spend eternity with Jesus is worth any cost. Anything I have to do will be forgotten when I come face to face with Him. I'm finding that necklace.

Evan rushes back to continue searching for the talisman. Sean sits back down. He crumples up the existing plan and throws it into a wastebasket.

SEAN. New plan.

MELISSA. Okay—fine. I didn't want to start a revolt against a demon anyway. Fine. I'll just . . . read a book.

Sean and Evan pay her no attention. Melissa pulls a book off the shelf.

MELISSA. *(Reading aloud.)* "The Sparkly Boy and the Furry Man: An Erotic Paddington Bear Fan Fiction." Ew.

Melissa sets the book down and picks up another. She flips through the pages and sets the book aside, then another book, and another.

MELISSA. And—they're all Paddington Bear erotica. And a Bible. Jesus, we are in Hell.

Act 1, Scene 10

Brimstone Hall, Room 664, a couple hours later. Melissa lies on top of the bed, evidently reading the Paddington Bear erotica. Evan has moved somewhere else in the room, tearing apart everything in his wake—the only place he hasn't searched yet is the wall. Sean continues scribbling away at his master plan.

EVAN. *(Singing, to himself.)*
"When peace, like a river, attendeth my way—
When sorrows like sea billows roll—
Whatever my lot, Thou has taught me to say,
'It is well, it is well, with my soul.'
It is well . . . (it is well)
With my soul . . . (with my soul)
It is well, it is well with my soul"

Sean smiles. He gets up and crosses to Evan.

SEAN. You're sounding good.

EVAN. Oh—thanks! Yeah, I love that old hymn. Keeps me calm when, uh, I think something's not right.

SEAN. *(Grins.)* Bet that's been stuck in your head since we got here, huh?

EVAN. Yeah, believe it or not!

SEAN. You're not too hard to read.

EVAN. I can't believe I haven't found this thing yet. I'm getting—*(Yawns.)* I'm just tired.

SEAN. Why not wait and take a break? You do look exhausted. Maybe get back at it tomorrow?

EVAN. I don't know, man, if I take a break, are you just gonna swoop in and find it in two seconds?

SEAN. Game respects game. I'll hold off until you're ready. Scout's honor.

A beat.

EVAN. Hey—uh. Can I share my testimony with you?

SEAN. Your what?

EVAN. My testimony. Everyone's got one, it's just the answer to the question: How did Jesus touch your life?

SEAN. Clearly not enough. We're in Hell.

Sean laughs.

EVAN. I share it with all my friends, usually right after meeting them.

SEAN. Sure, knock yourself out.

EVAN. *(Scripted.)* Well—I grew up in a Christian home. My dad is the senior pastor of Tapestry—that's a body of three thousand believers in my hometown. But yeah, even as a PK (pastor's kid) I was just kind of a lukewarm Christian for most of my life, man. I'd hear, but I didn't really listen. My dad was the picture of fatherhood, a strong Biblical man, teaching me to be exactly like him. I wish I was athletic like him—

SEAN. Why?

EVAN. *(Continued.)* I'd just—I've always struggled with not feeling man enough, you know? Like my dad loves football, and so do both my brothers and they're younger than me. But all I ever cared about was music.

SEAN. Oh, is that your major? At Freedom?

Evan is stunned that Sean interrupted him with a clarification question.

EVAN. No, I'm a Biblical studies major. You have any idea what people would think if I were a music major?

SEAN. That you're a guy who's good at music?

EVAN. Yeah. I don't know. *(Returns to his corny, scripted intonation.)* I'd hear my dad preach the gospel every moment of every day—but I didn't really listen until I was fifteen. Heck, I was just a kid. I was at Camp Whitestone, and my counselor just spoke into me and I really heard the voice of God right there in the woods. I wanted to give back so I became a counselor and worked there for three summers. I could go on and on and on about my years at camp . . .

The lights cut out. An hour goes by of Evan rambling on and on of directionless oversharing to Sean, who nonetheless listens intently. Melissa, meanwhile, shifts her position on the bed—she clearly hates the Paddington Bear erotica but she'd rather read that than the Bible. The lights come back on.

EVAN. . . . and yeah. So Jesus came into my life and lust is just—my cross to bear.

SEAN. What?

Evan spots the Bible on the end of Melissa's bed. He crosses to it.

EVAN. Is this—wow. A Bible? Maybe this is a sign . . .

Evan opens the Bible to a bookmarked page. He chokes up.

EVAN. And my life verse is bookmarked. "For I know the plans I have for you," declares the Lord, "plans to prosper you and not to harm you, plans to give you hope and a future."

SEAN. Well, that was a dumb verse to pick.

EVAN. Why would you say that? That's my life verse.

SEAN. You died.

Melissa closes her book and gets up from the bed.

MELISSA. So . . . why don't we think about—?

EVAN. It doesn't feel like a coincidence. Maybe Jesus is watching out for me, even in Hell. Do you have chills right now?

SEAN. Uh—no. I don't have chills.

Sean sticks his arm out.

SEAN. See? No chills. I'd definitely have gotten chills if my favorite verse was marked.

Sean takes the Bible from Evan. With a playful smirk, Sean flips to an earlier page in the Old Testament.

SEAN. Second Kings two, twenty-four. "He turned around, looked at them and called down a curse in the name of the Lord. Then two bears came out of the woods and mauled forty-two of the boys."

Sean beats his chest, indicating his heart.

SEAN. Speaks to me right here.

Evan bursts out laughing.

EVAN. What a classic!!

MELISSA. You guys are children.

Act 1, Scene 11

Brimstone Hall, Room 664, a couple hours later—night has fallen once again. Melissa, Evan, and Sean sit on the floor in a circle, this time playing strip poker. Evan is fully dressed, while Melissa and Sean are in varying stages of undress.

MELISSA. I'll see your watch—

Melissa removes her top and puts it in the center.

MELISSA. —and raise you a shirt.

EVAN. I'm uncomfortable.

SEAN. Oh, come on! *(Chanting.)* Daigle! Daigle! Daigle—

Evan smiles. He removes his shirt.

SEAN. Ohhhh!!!!

EVAN. One shirt. Show the cards?

Evan and Melissa reveal their cards.

MELISSA. Two pair. Sevens and Queens.

EVAN. I just had a King.

Sean reveals his cards.

SEAN. Royal Flush.

MELISSA. How?? You have to be rigging these cards.

SEAN. I don't win all the time. My win ratio's only two out of three. Every time. When I'm playing with competent people, anyway.

MELISSA. I can't. I can't with you.

Melissa crosses to her bed and lays down. Sean puts the cards away.

SEAN. Okay. Guess we're done.

EVAN. It has been a long day. I think I'll lie down. Mind if I take a pillow again, Seanathan?

Sean half-smiles.

SEAN. Dude, don't sleep on the floor. There's plenty of room on my bed.

EVAN. Uh—you sure? I—would that be weird?

SEAN. Come on, buddy.

Evan and Sean cross to bed.

SEAN. What do you think of your picture? Up there on the wall.

EVAN. Oh—I hadn't really, uh—looked at it much. That's my ID badge photo from Whitestone. I like it. It was my profile picture for a while.

SEAN. Mine's my headshot.

EVAN. You were arrested?

SEAN. *(Laughs.)* No. Headshot. Like, actors. My mom made me get it. It's kind of annoying seeing it here. But dude, Melissa—

Melissa rolls over, listening.

SEAN. She hates her picture.

EVAN. I don't think it's bad. I think she's pretty. She'd be even prettier if she were a Christian. Like if I weren't a Christian or if she were my wife—

SEAN. That's wild. I thought you hated her.

EVAN. No—I don't hate anybody, really. *(Pause.)* It's complicated. I think she's interesting. I've never seen a woman be so—forward. I don't think I like it but there's something—about it, you know? You get it.

SEAN. I guess.

Evan and Sean get into the bed, lying next to each other.

EVAN. Did everyone do what you expected today?

SEAN. For the most part, yeah. I didn't expect that she

would suggest we overthrow the demon—that came out of nowhere, but I did predict she would end up doing nothing. So it was always just you that I had to worry about.

EVAN. I'm flattered.

SEAN. Don't be. It's just a fact.

Evan and Sean fall asleep. Melissa gets out of bed. She puts her shirt back on and stares at her photo.

MELISSA. Ew, seriously? He likes that picture? Ay-yai-yai. Well. (*Looking at Evan's photo.*) He'd be prettier if he *weren't* a Christian. (*Looking at Sean's.*) A headshot, huh? His mom made him get it . . . (*Returns to her own photo.*) But, yeah, this one's gotta go.

Melissa removes the photo of herself from the wall. Behind the photo—of all places—is Teresa's talisman. Melissa tosses the photo aside.

MELISSA. Oh my god.

Melissa pulls the talisman off the wall and holds it up. The lights in the room may be dim, but the talisman shimmers. Goosebumps run up and down Melissa's arms.

MELISSA. You've got to be kidding me. Holy shit. *(Laughs.)* I just won. Wait—no. This has to be a trap. There's gotta be one behind each of these pictures.

Melissa removes the photos of Evan and Sean from the wall to find nothing behind either.

MELISSA. No? Just this one. This is it. I just won. *(Laughs.)* How ya like me now, Brother Christian? I'm gonna get to Heaven.

Melissa hears footsteps approaching—she haphazardly hangs all of the photos back on the wall. Teresa enters the room. Melissa quickly hides the talisman in her bra.

TERESA. Well. You're up late now, aren't you? A little talisman hunting while the boys are asleep?

MELISSA. Couldn't sleep. Did you know Brother Christian has a creepy crush on me? *(Indicates photo.)* And you've put this horny fodder in front of him so he can drool over me like a piece of meat? I wanna burn this. Got a light?

TERESA. You think he'd actually do that in front of you? There's nowhere to hide in this room.

MELISSA. Give us some time and he'll be comfortable enough. He's a man.

TERESA. *(Laughs.)* Maybe. I thought this picture was terrible—it was the first thing you noticed in this whole room.

MELISSA. There's a key difference between *my* worst picture and *the* worst picture.

TERESA. *(Grins.)* Anything else on your mind, Missy? Seems like you got something to say and ya just can't spit it out—

MELISSA. Okay. Fine. What happens when someone finds the necklace? Say Brother Christian found it. What if that happens? You'd really just beam him outta here?

TERESA. Yeah. He'd go to Heaven. Or you'd go to Heaven. Or Sean would go to Heaven. Honestly? My money's on Sean winning this any day of the week. But it doesn't matter. I get the last laugh. Because you see, handing me the talisman and going to Heaven means you'll be personally responsible for two others being tortured. Locked in a room with a demon at the height of her power for the rest of eternity. Evan's blood would be on your hands. Sean's blood would be on your hands. How could you live with that?

How could one person be so cruel as to hand the others an eternal sentence of cold-blooded torture?

Melissa looks at Evan and Sean, sleeping peacefully.

END OF ACT ONE.

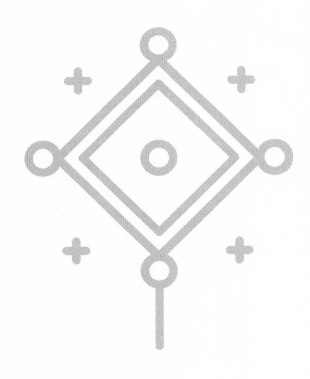

ACT TWO

SAUVIGNON BLANC

Act Two Preamble

BRIMSTONE HALL, *Room 664, continuous from the end of Act One. Melissa looks at Evan and Sean, sleeping peacefully.*

MELISSA. Well. I have a feeling I really shouldn't trust you.

TERESA. You've always had good instincts.

MELISSA. Okay. Say the person who found the necklace is willing to overlook the whole torture thing. What's holding you to keep your promise? Is there some massive chain of deals with the devil going on here?

TERESA. Nah. Just my word.

MELISSA. Your word means nothing to me. I think you're a fraud.

Teresa shrugs.

TERESA. Takes one to know one.

MELISSA. . . . What?

TERESA. Well, your word means nothing to me. I think *you're* a fraud.

MELISSA. Excuse me—how?

TERESA. I could spell it out for you, Missy Jones, but even if I did, I don't think you'd listen to me. But maybe you'd listen to you. Let me show you the day you died . . . Come on, I'm not gonna hurt ya any more than you hurt yourself.

MELISSA. Okay. Fine.

Melissa crosses to Teresa. Teresa wraps a blindfold around her.

TERESA. There. That's it—

CHAPTER FIVE:
AS MEDIATED BY
HOLLOW RHETORIC

The alarming case study of melissa Jones

The following chapter chronicles Melissa's memory of her final day on Earth. Mainstream pop music from the late 2010s plays in the background (something like Ariana Grande, Lizzo, or Taylor Swift). Melissa visualizes Evan as JASON, Teresa as both SUE-ELLEN and KRISTA, and Sean as ANDREW TSUI.

Act 2, Scene 1

BARCLAY SQUARE *Park in downtown Punxsutawney, Pennsylvania—a short drive from Punxsutawney College of Pennsylvania, late afternoon on Friday, October 11th. Melissa stands at the edge of the park, tapping her foot. JASON enters, carrying signs for a march protesting homelessness.*

MELISSA. Did we have to park so far away? My feet are killing me.

JASON. It was like seventeen bucks to park at the Police Department and come on—I'm not giving *the police* a dime—

MELISSA. Yeah, it just—

JASON. Oh my god. You think we should've paid?

MELISSA. Right now I wish we did. My legs are paying the price.

JASON. Well, I'll drive you right to your dorm. Carry you inside if I must.

MELISSA. Actually, I'll need you to drop me off at Andrew's.

JASON. Sure. Whatever you want.

Melissa pulls out her cell phone to check the time. She sighs.

MELISSA. Jesus. I'm gonna be late to my own birthday party.

JASON. I thought it didn't start until eight?

MELISSA. Yeah, but Andrew and I—we gotta set up, we

gotta pregame, we gotta—you know.

JASON. Ah yes. Andrew from . . . where'd you meet him?

MELISSA. BeezWax. It's Tinder for feminists.

JASON. And I guess it's going well if he's got a big chunk'a your birthday weekend—

MELISSA. Stop. He's good in bed. Buys me booze. Seems like he really likes me. What more could I ask for?

JASON. Who even is this guy? What's his deal?

MELISSA. He's a Punx alum, actually. Class of sixteen. He was in a frat, so. . .

JASON. Oh, which one?

MELISSA. Mmmmm—Sigmas, maybe? I don't know. Makes a lot of money now.

JASON. Doing what?

MELISSA. He's working—ah, what does he do? Something at a bank. Maybe a teller? . . . Oh! He's the head teller! At a bank. (*A beat.*) I don't know, he's got a nice office.

JASON. Think this one's gonna last?

MELISSA. Eh, who knows? Probably not. My sun's in Libra so I have really particular taste and interests and then I'm a very emotional person and I react big to everything because my moon's in Scorpio and I'm a Sagittarius rising—any long-term boyfriend of mine's gotta be a really good match, so with Andrew—we're basically star-crossed lovers. I'm here for a good time, not for a long one.

JASON. "Star-crossed lovers" . . . sounds a little dramatic.

MELISSA. I mean, if our signs mean anything, if we stay together long enough, one of us is probably gonna die.

Jason laughs.

JASON. Oh yeah? And when do you plan to tell him that?

MELISSA. I can wait a minute—it's my birthday tomorrow.

Melissa and Jason laugh. SUE-ELLEN enters.

SUE-ELLEN. Excuse me. I don't mean to offend or bother.

I'm really struggling. If either of you could find it in your heart to help me get something to eat or drink—

Jason and Melissa look at each other. Melissa contorts her face.

MELISSA. Come on, let's go.

Jason sets the protest signs down and tosses his car keys to Melissa.

JASON. I'll get a ride back to campus. See you at the party. *(To Sue-Ellen.)* Come on, let's get you some food.

SUE-ELLEN. Oh, God bless you!

Jason exits with Sue-Ellen. Melissa stands, watching, holding the car keys.

Act 2, Scene 2

The living room of Andrew Tsui's apartment near Punxsutawney College of Pennsylvania, early evening on Friday, October 11th. Melissa watches as ANDREW enters in his boxers from the bedroom, putting his pants back on. He crosses to Melissa and kisses her. Andrew runs his fingers through Melissa's hair.

ANDREW. Your picture from the march. I've been thinking about it all day, waiting to see you.

Melissa pulls out her phone and checks the social media app.

MELISSA. I looked cute in this one. Ugh—why hasn't anyone liked it?

ANDREW. Looks like seventy-three people did.

MELISSA. Yeah. Seventy-three.

Melissa taps her phone. Andrew grins.

ANDREW. Refreshing the app over and over isn't gonna generate likes.

MELISSA. Ha! Sabrina from my floor last year just liked it. And so did Hayley!

ANDREW. How was the march?

MELISSA. Yeah, it was good.

ANDREW. You're one of a kind . . . spending part of your birthday weekend to help the homeless.

MELISSA. It's in my blood—reminded me of marching with my mom in Philly. If I don't stand up for homeless women in the Pittsburgh metro, who will?

ANDREW. There's my social justice warrior. *(Separate thought.)* When we get the chance, I really want you to show me around Philly sometime. I've always wanted to run up the Rocky steps.

MELISSA. Let's get through my birthday, then we can make plans.

Andrew kisses Melissa on the cheek.

ANDREW. Can't wait to meet all your friends.

MELISSA. They'll be too drunk to remember you.

ANDREW. But they'll know I'm the guy who bought all the booze.

MELISSA. There's my sugar daddy.

ANDREW. You make it sound like I'm forty. You gotta hurry up and turn twenty-one, babe. But I can settle for twenty. People give me shit when they hear my girlfriend's nineteen.

MELISSA. You're telling people about me?

ANDREW. Only when I'm bragging about some clever revolutionary at Punxsutawney. I've invited a few friends to our party.

A beat.

ANDREW. What are you thinking?

MELISSA. It's cute. You'll have to introduce me to . . . all of your friends.

Melissa runs her fingers up and down Andrew's chest.

MELISSA. But you know what I wanna do? Right now?

ANDREW. Again?

MELISSA. No—let's get me to this rooftop party. I'll drink, maybe a little too much—come back to your place. Put on a movie, fall asleep on top of you. I'd like that.

Andrew smiles.

ANDREW. I'd like that, too.

Act 2, Scene 3

The roof of Andrew Tsui's apartment building near Punxsutawney College of Pennsylvania, a few hours later on the night of Friday, October 11th. Guarding the edge of the roof is a ficus tree, set near a modest table of liquor selections. KRISTA is at the liquor table, pouring herself a drink. Andrew and Melissa enter —Melissa is now properly dressed for the party.

MELISSA. I didn't realize you had so many friends. So many people who know about us. That's . . . so fun.

ANDREW. I think you really hit it off with Connor and Alisha—we should hang out with them sometime. Maybe over your fall break—

MELISSA. What an idea.

Krista spots Andrew and Melissa.

KRISTA. Andrew!!

Krista crosses to Andrew and Melissa and gives Andrew a big hug.

ANDREW. Hey!! So happy you made it!

KRISTA. And this must be the birthday girl!

ANDREW. Yeah. Melissa, this is Krista—

KRISTA. I've heard so much about you.

MELISSA. Oh—how do you guys know each other?

Krista laughs.

ANDREW. We dated in undergrad for like—how long was it, babe?

KRISTA. Two years, give or take? Don't worry, we only broke up because—timing, really. Andrew's awesome. Nothing but the best for you two.

ANDREW. I think you two would get along really well, actually—Krista's getting her PhD in psychology and does a lot of social justice-y research. Didn't you just present something?

KRISTA. Yes, I was at a conference last weekend in Ft. Lauderdale! I presented my paper, "Women Who Use Men: The Differential Effects of Coercion as Mediated by Hollow Rhetoric."

ANDREW. What'd you find?

KRISTA. There's actually this fascinating correlation between women who fail to follow through on their stated beliefs and them being "users" of their male partners.

Melissa shifts; uncomfortable.

KRISTA. It's so important that young women understand that building themselves up doesn't mean tearing anyone else down—other women, men, anyone outside the binary. Equality and progress literally can't happen on systemic levels if we say all the right things but don't mean them, wouldn't you say?

ANDREW. *(To Melissa.)* Everything okay?

MELISSA. Yep! I'm just—at my birthday party, feeling great. I'm gonna need another vodka cider. Back in a sec.

Melissa crosses to the liquor table. She pours nearly a full red solo cup of some cheap vodka and tops it with a little hit of apple cider. Melissa chugs the drink as she watches Andrew and Krista continue talking, almost as if they'd never broken up at all.

ANDREW. Your paper wasn't inspired by our relationship,

was it?

KRISTA. Ha! No, of course not! The hundred or so relationships I interviewed were mostly situations where—

Krista continues. Melissa eyes the ficus tree and crosses to it.

MELISSA. What a perfect view of downtown!

Melissa looks out over the edge.

MELISSA. Babe!! Take my picture?

KRISTA. I actually got a call earlier this week that someone nominated my work for a TED Talk!

ANDREW. Whoa, that's incredible!

MELISSA. Andrew—get over here, it's perfect!

Melissa stares across the rooftop at Andrew and Krista, chatting away. She rolls her eyes.

MELISSA. I'll just do it myself. Taking a selfie at my own party—

Melissa pulls out her phone and strikes a pose. She leans back and dangles off the edge, snapping the photo. She loses her balance.

MELISSA. *(Vocalizing distress.)* Ah—uh—

ANDREW. You're gonna be a thought leader. Congrats!

KRISTA. Thanks! Dr. Steggerda has been a great advisor, really pushing me—

MELISSA. Help!!

Melissa tries to grab the ficus tree as leverage. She falls backward off the roof, screaming—twice. Andrew and Krista rush over. Andrew looks down to the street. It's too late.

ANDREW. Oh my god!!

Chapter Six:
Blossom of Snow

Act 2, Scene 4

BRIMSTONE HALL, *Room 664, continuous from before Melissa's flashback. Sean and Evan are asleep together in one twin bed. Teresa stands next to Melissa, who is blindfolded. Melissa removes the blindfold.*

MELISSA. Ridiculous.

TERESA. If it's any consolation, the selfie turned out great!

MELISSA. You're just cherry-picking everything you showed to make me look problematic.

TERESA. I don't know what you're talking about, that pretty much summed up who you were. I even let you see your boyfriend's horrified face as he watched you fall to your death. A two-screamer! What more do you want?

MELISSA. Show me an entire week.

TERESA. You've got nothing to prove! You belong here and I know why. And I'm starting to think you do, too. How long were you seeing that hunk of man candy Andrew Tsui from BeezWax?

MELISSA. We matched the first week of the semester.

TERESA. Interesting. So that's what? Six weeks?

MELISSA. Yeah. Why do you care?

TERESA. Interesting. Interesting. I'm no human woman, but it seemed like he cared for you.

MELISSA. What are you trying to say?

TERESA. Nothing really. I'd just think what a person does for a living would come up a couple times, if you're seeing each other for six weeks. You know I've heard someone say something like there's this fascinating correlation between women who don't mean what they say and—

MELISSA. Oh my god, why would you—? Of course I cared about Andrew. I tried to make the world a better place. I marched for homeless women in Pittsburgh.

TERESA. Yes. And you donated money—which, good for you, girl! Coming from that working-class family in Philly, gonna run for office someday and make a difference in the world for women everywhere. *Truly* selfless.

MELISSA. Why does it sound like you're mocking me?

TERESA. I'm just saying everything you say about yourself, practically verbatim. Just between you and me? I know you. You say you want what's best for everyone—but at the end of the day, you only care about number one. And, just spitballing here, if my talisman were hiding in your bra right now, I know exactly what you'd do.

MELISSA. You're wrong.

TERESA. Then I wanna see it, Missy. Think about it. Think about it . . .

Teresa exits. Melissa stands at center stage, pulls the talisman out of her bra, and stares at it.

Act 2, Scene 5

Brimstone Hall, Room 664, the next morning. Melissa still stands at center stage, staring at the talisman in her hand. Sean and Evan have gotten up and are back in their usual spots: Evan tearing the room apart, searching desperately for his ticket into Heaven, and Sean sitting at the desk, scribbling down new strategies as he watches every move Evan makes like a hawk. Neither Sean nor Evan has noticed Melissa holding the talisman in her hand.

EVAN. *(Singing, loudly—unhinged.)*
    "And Lord—haste the day when my faith shall be sight,
    The clouds be rolled back as a scroll,
    The *TRUMP* shall resound and my Lord shall descend—
    Even so, it is well with my soul."

Sean and Melissa both bristle at Evan's special emphasis on the name of the 45th President of the United States.

EVAN. *(Continued, unhinged singing.)*
    "It is well . . . (it is well)
    With my soul . . . (with my soul)
    It is well, it is well with—"

Melissa hides the talisman on her person. She crosses to Evan.

MELISSA. Hey—would you mind, maybe—cooling it with the singing for a little? I didn't sleep at all last night.

EVAN. Fine. I just can't believe it's been three days tearing apart this tiny room. How the *heck* have I not found this thing yet?

MELISSA. I don't know. Maybe . . . what if there is no necklace? Like, what if she made it all up?

EVAN. No. I can't afford to think that. Knowing there's hope . . . that I could come face to face with Jesus. That's what's keeping me together. I'll never give up until the battle is won.

MELISSA. Sometimes I wish I had that kind of faith.

Evan's face lights up.

EVAN. Have you heard the Gospel of Jesus before? See, the story of God's love for mankind can be broken down into four simple words: Lord-Sin-Savior-Faith. It's never too late to turn your heart to Jesus, repent of your sins, and—

MELISSA. Blind optimism. I wish I had that kind of blind optimism. I forgot how loaded that word *faith* is for you people.

EVAN. It's everything!

MELISSA. Yeah.

EVAN. Jesus is Lord of all creation but our sin is what separates us from Him. Sin can be traced back to Eve in the Garden of Eden when she—

Evan trails off as he continues spouting his standard verbal presentation of the Gospel. Melissa crosses to Sean.

MELISSA. Just curious. What did you do for a living?

SEAN. Nothing. I was a student at Edgemere.

MELISSA. Right. But why bother going to an Ivy if you could make it as an actor?

A beat. Sean sets his pen down.

SEAN. How do you know about me?

MELISSA. Um—I don't. You just sorta have the—look. And I overheard you say last night your picture—on the wall. It's a headshot? I assumed you're an actor.

SEAN. I'm not. *(A beat.)* My mom is.

MELISSA. Oh, would I know her?

Sean pauses.

SEAN. My full name is Sean Liu-Ogden.

Melissa's eyes widen.

MELISSA. Holy shit. Hey, Brother Christian! Sean's famous!

EVAN. Oh. Wait, really?

MELISSA. His mom is *Elsa Liu*!

EVAN. . . . Am I supposed to know who that is?

MELISSA. She's one of the highest-paid actresses in Hollywood. How could you not know Elsa Liu?

EVAN. I was raised in a bubble.

MELISSA. She was like *the* Asian "it girl" of the late nineties. American producer scoops her out of her modeling contract in China to star in *Peking Noir*, he starts sleeping with her, and she wins an Oscar while she's seven months pregnant with his baby—oh! That was probably you, Sean!

SEAN. Obviously, that's my mom, so by process of elimi—

MELISSA. Oh my god, it was *so messy*! This guy had left his first wife of like twenty-five years for her. Netflix even made a tell-all docu-series about her marriage to James Ogden. She's one of those celebrities you don't expect would be funny but every time she posts, I laugh my ass off. So that must be where I've seen you before! I've been following Elsa Liu all these years. Basically watched you grow up with me. And that's why you're so hot. Okay, I get it.

SEAN. Yeah. Thanks.

MELISSA. Probably had no trouble getting into Edgemere, then. Everyone knows that story. Kid from a rich family buys his way into the country's best education while the rest of us barely afford a state school working three jobs—

SEAN. *(Angry.)* You don't get to be Valedictorian if you didn't work. I was a straight-A student, dual-enrollment, National Honor Society president, student council president, and played varsity tennis all four years. I did lighting design for the fall play. I applied to every single Ivy. But the only school I got into was my father's. James Ogden's an Edgemere, so naturally—

EVAN. James Ogden?

SEAN. My dad, obviously. Writer. Producer. Director. Moved from Hollywood to Atlanta when it became a film haven in the late seventies with all the tax breaks. Founded Ogden Peach Pictures, made a fortune. Mom ran into his arms, and the rest is history.

EVAN. Huh. My friend's family is famous. Cool.

Evan resumes tearing the room apart. Sean resumes scribbling.

SEAN. I shouldn't have reacted like that. Elsa Liu is my mom. James Ogden is my dad. There's no point in being angry about objective facts—

MELISSA. Yeah, I don't know how anyone could be mad if Elsa Liu was their mom—

SEAN. I'm my own person, okay? I don't spend my life making things up or telling a camera crew my entire life story. That's not my life! You think I wanted any of this?

Working with real things and solving real problems seems like a better way to spend time and money anyway.

MELISSA. Speaking of real things . . . What's going on with you two?

SEAN. Evan? Uh . . . what do you mean?

MELISSA. He seems to think you're friends . . . and I'd be lying if I said I didn't notice . . . something there.

SEAN. I'm still trying to predict his behavior. Running lots of game theory scenarios. He's a simple guy. Easy to predict.

MELISSA. A simple guy worth (*Looks at Sean's stack of notes.*) what, fifteen pages of notes? Someone's a little obsessed—

SEAN. Well, no. Obviously. I have to think about what he's going to do, which in turn I can then put myself in the best position to win. Every single time.

MELISSA. Two out of three times, right?

SEAN. Incorrect. I put myself in the *position* to win every single time. I actually win two out of three times.

MELISSA. My god.

Melissa grabs a notecard off Sean's desk.

MELISSA. So what do your notes on me look like?

SEAN. Give that back—

MELISSA. *(Reading aloud.)* "Piece of work."

SEAN. I call 'em like I see 'em.

MELISSA. What's with this? You claim to be this fair, objective, balanced voice of reason—but I know for a fact that's not true! You've dismissed every single thing I've said this whole time when you have the patience to let Brother Christian talk airy Jesus nonsense at you for hours?

SEAN. It wasn't . . . hours.

MELISSA. You hang on every word he says! What's with that? You have Brother Christian willingly jumping into bed with you when you won't even—

SEAN. It's not like that, okay?

Sean resumes note-taking.

SEAN. In case you were wondering.

MELISSA. Not like . . . what?

Sean ignores Melissa. She gives up. Sean drifts off into his own world—completely thrown off by everything that just happened. Melissa crosses to Evan.

MELISSA. So you and Sean are friends, right?

EVAN. Yeah, Sean's really cool! I told him my testimony and I really got to just be vulnerable and—

MELISSA. I know. I was there. What do you think will happen if you get the necklace?

EVAN. I'll be face to face with God Himself.

MELISSA. But you realize if you take that ticket to Heaven —you're also deciding Sean gets tortured for eternity.

EVAN. Well—if in the end, I'm in Heaven—

MELISSA. I just—I would have a hard time saying I deserve eternal punishment that much less than you and Sean. The ends do not, and never, justify the means.

EVAN. But finding the necklace is the right thing to do . . . because I love the Lord my God. You know, the greatest commandment is love the Lord your God with all your heart, soul, mind, and strength—

Melissa gives up and lies on the bed, moping.

EVAN. —but the next is love your neighbor as yourself. So who, then, is my neighbor? . . . If I saw either Sean or Melissa bleeding on the side of the road, attacked by robbers —of course I'd help them. So they're both my neighbors. What would Jesus do? What does Jesus want me to do? This is how we know what love is—that he lay down his life for his friend. Sean is my friend . . . Melissa's . . . a person. And if all people bear the image of God . . . Oh God. Even if I found it—the most Christlike thing to do would be give it away, isn't it? It's what Jesus would do. That's literally what Jesus did. Oh God. Lord—what do I do?

------◆------

Act 2, Scene 6

Brimstone Hall, Room 664, a few hours later. No one has moved since the end of the previous scene—Melissa lies on the bed, filled with angst. Evan stands with the mess he's made tearing apart the room, wracked with shame. Sean sits at the desk, frozen in fear. Teresa enters with a smug, toothy grin on her face.

TERESA. Good evening! Are we all making ourselves truly miserable yet?

Teresa scans the room to see just that. Her grin widens.

TERESA. Oh good!

Melissa rises, burning with fury, and makes a beeline to Teresa.

MELISSA. Was this your plan all along?

TERESA. Most of it, yeah.

MELISSA. You're a monster. These boys aren't really being tortured. And if I didn't know better, I'd say they're the real demons. Religious and rich. Sean thinks I'm a vapid party girl, Brother Christian thinks I'm the Whore of Babylon. You know—you—you got in my head and made me think I'm some problematic asshat and that I needed to change something—

TERESA. I'm your guardian—that's my job.

MELISSA. But for what? Seriously, for what? So I can sit in this room forever with two guys who aren't gonna listen to me? Or notice that I'm trying? Trying to actually be everything I said I was? Because if this is what eternity's going to feel like, you did it. Congratulations. You *fucking* did it. I've been here three days and I wanna somehow die again.

TERESA. OK, this pity party's gotta stop. And besides. If everything's going to plan—

Evan crosses to Sean. Teresa points to them.

TERESA. This should be interesting no matter how it plays out.

SEAN. Uh—hey, man.

EVAN. Sean, I need to tell you something—

SEAN. Oh, yeah?

EVAN. It's, uh—completely going against my self-interest, but . . . that's kind of the point. If everyone, truly everyone, is equal in the eyes of God . . . then I don't think I could ever say that someone like you deserves to be tortured forever

more than me. So . . . if I find the necklace. I'm going to . . .
I'm gonna give it to you.

SEAN. W-what? Why?

EVAN. If I pushed someone deeper into Hell to secure my
spot in Heaven . . . then Jesus would've taught me nothing.

SEAN. I—I can't accept this.

Sean gets up and turns away.

MELISSA. Whoa, what's going on?

Tears roll down Sean's cheek. Teresa crosses to Sean.

TERESA. Buddy. It's okay. Let it out.

SEAN. *(Incoherent babbling.)* You're . . . I lo— I don't— I don't
know anyone who would . . . how could I? It's, it's— I just—
It's—

Melissa beams. Sean's heart pounds.

MELISSA. Oh my god—now it all makes sense! You're gay,
aren't you? Not that that's a big deal, but you're gay.

Evan's face washes over.

SEAN. No. (*Pause.*) I'm not gay.

TERESA. What do you think about gay people, Sean? Just, like, in general?

SEAN. They should be free to live however they choose. It's not up to me to say whether that's a good or bad thing.

TERESA. Hmm. Okay. So, if that's the case, how would you describe what you went through when Jake moved away? Or when Brent started dating Cassie? Or . . .

SEAN. Feelings are irrelevant. And dating is like getting a part-time job, but the money flows the wrong way.

TERESA. Deep down, somewhere—under all those layers of theory . . . you know that's not true.

A beat. Sean shakes his head.

TERESA. Adam Weaver was with you when you died. Right there by your side to the very last breath.

SEAN. So? Why would I care about him any more than any other fr—?

TERESA. I'll show you right now. Close your eyes and hold real still—yeah, just like that.

Sean lets his guard down and closes his eyes. Teresa wraps a blindfold around him.

CHAPTER SEVEN: BLACK-BOTTOM HAZELNUT PIE

The Lovestruck Tragedy of Sean Liu

The following chapter chronicles Sean's memory of his final day on Earth. Plucky banjo rural folk music plays in the background. Sean visualizes Evan as ADAM WEAVER, Teresa as JOYCE WEAVER, and Melissa as DANNI.

Act 2, Scene 7

THE KITCHEN *in Randy and Joyce Weaver's house in Lancaster County, Pennsylvania, on the morning of Friday, October 11th. It's fall break for Edgemere University. Sean comes down a flight of stairs as ADAM and JOYCE talk in the kitchen.*

Sean stops on the stairs to eavesdrop.

ADAM. Honestly, Mom—he could be. It's hard to think about him dating anyone, though—doesn't talk about guys or girls, really. He's usually just studying or gaming. Talks to his mom a lot.

111

JOYCE. I knew I liked him.

ADAM. Yeah, seems like a good guy. I, uh . . . definitely want to get to know him better.

Sean's heart flutters. Sean finishes coming down the stairs to meet Adam and Joyce.

JOYCE. Well, it'll be interesting no matter how this plays out. And, speak of the devil! Good morning, Sean! How did you sleep?

SEAN. Oh yeah, I slept great. Felt like I was right at home.

JOYCE. Sorry again about the pink sheets.

SEAN. It was fine, thank you.

JOYCE. Can I—?

SEAN. Given those were the only sheets that were clean that fit your daughter's bed, there wouldn't be any incentive for you to wash a different set of sheets, using up water, detergent, whatever and then take a guess on what color I like, when at the end of the day—they're just sheets.

ADAM. He's like this about everything, Mom. Nothing's an easy decision or simple answer. What is your favorite color, anyway? Blue?

SEAN. I don't really have one.

ADAM. Who doesn't have a favorite color?

SEAN. There's no point in picking a favorite color, unless it becomes a game—like if I knew you were going to guess my favorite color and I had incentive for you to be wrong, my optimal strategy would be to pick yellow or purple since very few people pick those two—

JOYCE. Can I get you something for breakfast? I just made some toast for Adam . . . he likes it with peanut butter and Nutella—

SEAN. Oh—thank you, but I have a really bad hazelnut allergy. Like, there's a non-zero chance if I ever eat hazelnut again, it would kill me.

JOYCE. Well. I don't like those odds. How about some eggs? Scrambled?

SEAN. Yes, please.

JOYCE. I'm very happy to meet you, Sean, but remind me why you didn't go home for fall break?

SEAN. Oh, my mom's off in the Bay Area filming some Indie project—

JOYCE. Wait, no—don't tell me. Adam said your mom is the woman from—

SEAN. Elsa Liu. Detective Zhang from that movie *Peking Noir.*

JOYCE. Oh my gosh! That's so cool! Didn't that win an Oscar or something?

SEAN. Yep. Best Picture. Mom won Best Supporting.

JOYCE. I didn't realize she was still doing stuff—

SEAN. She does a lot of guest spots on TV shows and she did like six movies last year, but they're mostly crap. Made-for-TV. But basically, my choices were either to sit in my room and do nothing, or fly to Atlanta, sit in my room, and do nothing.

JOYCE. Wouldn't it be nice to see your dad?

SEAN. He's busy all the time. I'll see him at Christmas. It was obviously much less time and money wasted to stay in the area. And I—I think I'd always be willing to do something spontaneous with Adam.

Joyce smiles.

ADAM. I'm flattered. Mom—can you get those eggs started? Fair opens in twenty minutes and it's an hour drive —

JOYCE. Okay, okay—it's gonna be there all day!

Joyce cracks an egg into a measuring cup. Adam grins.

ADAM. Sean, what are the odds you eat that egg raw?

SEAN. "The odds?" What are you talking about?

ADAM. Oh! Dude, you're gonna love this. So I dare you to do something stupid and ask you "what are the odds?" And then you give me a number, like "one in twenty," or something, and then when I count to three, we both say a number between one and twenty. If we match, then you gotta do it. So what are the odds you eat that egg raw, mister?

Sean grins.

SEAN. Okay. One in… five.

ADAM. One, two, three—

SEAN. *(Simultaneously.)* Four.

ADAM. *(Simultaneously.)* Four.

SEAN. Oh my god.

ADAM. Mom—don't cook that egg.

Act 2, Scene 8

The South-Central Lancaster County Fair, a couple hours later —mid-afternoon on Friday, October 11th. Adam and Sean are having a blast together—they've literally been playing "What Are the Odds?" all day long. Sean points in the distance at a little petting zoo area.

SEAN. What are the odds that you touch that mini-horse's butt?

ADAM. Eww! One in . . . five thousand.

SEAN. Really? Five-thousand? *(Playfully smirking.)* Coward.

ADAM. Fine. Okay. One in thirty-nine.

SEAN. Okay. One-two-three—

ADAM. *(Simultaneously.)* Seventeen.

SEAN. *(Simultaneously.)* Seventeen.

Sean laughs.

ADAM. Dammit, Sean. Eh—Okay.

Adam and Sean cross to the petting zoo. Adam reaches into the pen to touch the mini-horse. It whinnies. Adam runs away. Sean laughs.

ADAM. Gross.

SEAN. Poor horse is probably scarred for life.

ADAM. Yeah, I can't look that thing in the eye.

Adam looks around. He sees a funnel cake stand.

ADAM. OK, Seanathan—

SEAN. (*Grinning.*) "Seanathan."

ADAM. —what are the odds that you stick your hand in that deep fryer?

Sean moves closer to Adam.

SEAN. What are the odds that was a serious bet?

Sean and Adam stand face to face, locking eye contact.

ADAM. Oh, I'm dead serious—I wanna see you stick your hand in that deep fryer.

Sean grins.

SEAN. Okay, mister. Maybe I will. One in two.

ADAM. You remember when it's one in two—if we say different numbers, then I have to do it.

Sean raises his eyebrow.

SEAN. I know.

ADAM. Sean.

SEAN. Adam.

ADAM. I'm not sticking my hand in that deep fryer.

SEAN. Ohhhh!! I called the bluff!

Adam nudges Sean playfully.

Act 2, Scene 9

The South-Central Lancaster County Fair, a couple of hours later—it's early evening on Friday, October 11th. Sean and Adam have wandered into an area with a stage and a small crowd gathered watching local radio personality DANNI standing in front of a table with a covered monstrosity. Sean and Adam don't initially see her, facing a different direction. Sean scans the area to find a new challenge for Adam.

SEAN. Okay. What are the odds that you—?

DANNI. Step on up, y'all!!

119

Sean and Adam turn to listen.

DANNI. Step right on up!! FM 95.3 presents the ultimate dare and challenge at the South-Central Lancaster County Fair—introducing the Worley Pie House's diabolical new creation, The Great American Dumpster-Fire!

Danni reveals the pie—it's multiple layers high, like the leaning tower of Pisa. She pulls out a lighter and sets the very top of the pie on fire.

ADAM. Holy shit!

DANNI. Whoever can eat this entire monstrosity in ninety seconds wins a t-shirt and a Worley Pie House woodpecker!

Danni pulls out a giant teddy bear-like plush bird, wearing its own Worley Pie House t-shirt. Adam laughs, dismissive.

ADAM. I want that woodpecker.

DANNI. The Great American Dumpster-Fire is a seven-layer beast, starting with a scoop of red-hot cinnamon firecracker ice cream right on top . . .

Danni continues to describe the other layers.

ADAM. Yo. I'd be really impressed to see someone finish. Man, they'd be my hero.

SEAN. I'd do it. I'll be your hero.

ADAM. Wait. Really? Not a bluff? Dude . . . what are the odds?

Sean locks eyes with Adam, giving him a longing, loving stare— conspicuously not hearing Danni's next line. Adam doesn't hear it either.

DANNI. . . . and it's all piled on top of Grandma Worley's signature Black-Bottom Hazelnut Pie—a family recipe since 1937!

SEAN. One in one. I'm doing it.

ADAM. Why?

SEAN. *(Shrugs.)* Easy decision, simple answer.

DANNI. Who's gonna step on up and take on the Great American Dum—?

Sean crosses to Danni.

SEAN. I volunteer as tribute.

DANNI. We've got our first challenger, ready to take on this big ol' Hunger Game! Damn, you look familiar. Have I seen you before?

SEAN. My name is Sean Liu-Ogden. I'm from Atlanta.

DANNI. And tell me, Sean, I can't imagine a boy as good-looking as you is here alone. You got some special gal out there in the crowd?

SEAN. N-nope.

Sean stares directly into Adam's eyes, his heart pounding.

SEAN. Just my best friend.

DANNI. How sweet. Gather 'round, one and all—Sean from Atlanta's takin' on the Great American Dumpster-Fire!! He's single, ladies!

Joyce enters. Sean sits at the table with the pie in front of him. Joyce joins Adam.

DANNI. All righty, Sean—ninety seconds on the clock.

Ready! Set!

Sean dives right into the pie. He is only looking at Adam—Sean pays no attention to what he's eating.

DANNI. And we're off to the races already! No time to lose for this out-of-towner—he has completely scarfed down the top layers and is starting to go to town on the pie—yes, folks, Sean is like a machine tearing into that base layer of the signature Black-Bottom Hazelnut Pie—

ADAM. Hazelnut?

Terror washes over Adam and Joyce's faces. Sean has sudden trouble breathing. Sean stares directly at Adam.

SEAN. (*Choked out.*) Adam—

DANNI. We've hit a little snag—looks like our boy has bit off more than he can chew! Let's see how—

Danni trails off as she realizes this is serious. Sean shakes violently, hyperventilating in horrible pain.

JOYCE. Someone call 911!

We hear an ambulance approaching. Sean faints, with a fall to the ground. Adam hurries to Sean's side and kneels down, bending over the body.

ADAM. Sean??

A beat. Adam's heart splits in two.

A tear rolls down Adam's cheek.

ADAM. Sean?

Chapter Eight:
Dead Silence

Act 2, Scene 10

BRIMSTONE HALL, *Room 664, continuous from before Sean's flashback. Dead silence all around. Melissa and Evan watch as Teresa stands next to a blindfolded Sean. Sean removes the blindfold. He's right on the verge of crying.*

SEAN. You lied to me.

TERESA. What are you talking about? He was right there— you died in his arms.

SEAN. You said I choked on pie. But that was like ninety percent ganache. There's no way I could've choked. That was anaphylactic shock—

TERESA. Small detail. Trust me: it was so much more fun to say you choked on pie!

The tears start falling from Sean's eyes. Sean wipes the tears away.

SEAN. I should've known it was hazelnut.

TERESA. You know, you're a very smart boy when you think with your brain, Sean.

SEAN. What else would I think with? My heart?

TERESA. Sure, let's go with "heart." You loved him.

Sean shakes his head.

TERESA. You know, like it or not, you earned your spot at Edgemere. Someone like Melissa would've killed to get into your school—but the facts speak for themselves. Legacy or not, you did it.

SEAN. Yeah. So?

TERESA. It's an objective fact. You're smart. You're a hard worker. What's the point of getting angry about objective facts?

SEAN. Yeah. Okay. I see what you're doing here.

TERESA. As you just saw—you loved Adam.

SEAN. But I'm not gay.

TERESA. Why's that bother you so much? The possibility that you could be gay? The facts speak for themselves: over several male friendships, very much including Adam Weaver, you developed feelings—

SEAN. Feelings are irrelevant.

Dead silence.

SEAN. You can't quantify or control them, therefore they can't be explained. They shouldn't factor into how you understand where you fit into reality around you. So: Given I know that I didn't choose to be gay, and feelings are out of my control and irrelevant, therefore I can't be gay. *(Tearing up.)* Who would even choose to be gay? Mom—she would've had even more of an excuse to use me as a prop for her millions of followers. "Look at how good a mom I am—I love my gay son!" Don't even wanna know what my dad would think. Not that I care. But even just out there in the world, people—they—they stare. They look at two guys, when they hold hands. Or when they kiss. Gay guys are all— big and they're loud. And artsy and—I don't want any of

127

that. I want a normal life that I built on my own. Not because of my dad. Not because of my . . . heart. I just want to be left alone. *(Wipes a tear away.)* I wish there was a way to be with a guy, but . . . be straight.

Teresa hugs Sean.

EVAN. Does anyone else see what I'm seeing here?

MELISSA. Probably not.

EVAN. A demon—literally coddling someone who lost his battle with same-sex attraction. This is Hell. I—I get it now.

MELISSA. "Same-sex". . . What the f—?

EVAN. *(To Sean.)* All this time . . . you know, I've wondered about you. I've been wondering . . . what did you possibly do to get sent here? I thought maybe, maybe you were a mistake. Like me. You even had me fooled for a second. God, I shared a bed with you.

MELISSA. Oh please—I can name twenty reasons he deserves to be in Hell, but not a single one of them have a damn thing to do with him being gay. How old are you?

EVAN. The Truth of the Gospel doesn't go out of fashion.

MELISSA. Yeah, well, guess what? Your precious Gospel didn't save you. So maybe step all the way back? Literally five minutes ago, he was your best friend and you were ready to give up your spot in Heaven for him and now— have you considered that it wasn't a mistake that you're in Hell? Maybe that's why you're here?

EVAN. What do you mean?

MELISSA. Being so sure you know what your God thinks about everything. What's the point of pushing a person away just because he's gay? You're already in Hell with him. Why would you push *anyone* away? Obviously you've been wrong about something!

EVAN. You're wrong. I spent my last moments on Earth preaching the words of Jesus Christ.

MELISSA. How did you even die?

EVAN. I got hit by a bus.

MELISSA. Yeah, I know that, dumbass. What happened right before?

EVAN. My girlfriend broke up with me. She . . . also struggles with same-sex attraction.

MELISSA. So then, what? A bus had to mow you down for you to leave some poor lesbian alone?

EVAN. Hey, the gays are not some poor souls, they *choose* to not pursue victory over their sins.

MELISSA. How? How can you say that when it's so clear Sean didn't choose to be gay? Look at him, he's still crying!

EVAN. Oh my gosh! That's the reason I'm here—

Evan crosses to Sean.

EVAN. Sean. This is our chance. I can hold you accountable as my brother in Christ.

SEAN. . . . What?

EVAN. I will help you grow into manhood. We can reclaim your Biblical masculinity and redeem your lifestyle of sin—

TERESA. Oh my god, no. Do not do that. I know I'm supposed to remain impartial and everything as the

Guardian but—no. No. That's not why you're here, Evan, do not do that.

SEAN. Yeah—uh. Yeah. I'm good. You're behaving exactly as I expected. Actually.

EVAN. What do you mean?

SEAN. Given your positioning as a traditional values evangelical Christian who got really defensive about your own manhood despite having some stereotypically feminine interests . . . I would even say that you were jealous of my perceived masculinity—

EVAN. No. Not at all, because—

SEAN. Of course, I'm right. But your sudden change in attitude indicates to me that the only reason you saw me as a friend is that you thought I was straight. If that's the case, then it's really only a matter of time before that friendship stops when you learn that I'm—

TERESA. Seriously—no rush to label yourself—you literally have eternity to figure out what works!

EVAN. That's . . . interesting. I really did think you were a good friend. But unless you repent, I don't know if I'm willing to sacrifice my spot in Heaven for you. Both of you, living in sin. I'd have to pray on it if I find the necklace.

MELISSA. You won't.

EVAN. Have you no faith?

MELISSA. Of course not. I'm an atheist. But . . . more importantly . . .

Melissa pulls out the talisman.

MELISSA. I found this shiny boy all by myself.

SEAN. Holy shit!

TERESA. Congratulations, Melissa. You have won the game. You'll be going to Heaven now. Just hand me the talisman and up you go!

Melissa steps toward Teresa as she looks at the talisman in her hand.

MELISSA. You know, I could. I really could. I don't know. And there's a sadistic part of me that would do that willingly, even take a little pleasure going to paradise knowing a Christian bigot with no grip on reality and a rich smartass who gets his designer boxer-briefs in a twist about everything are getting tortured here in this room for eternity. But that's the part of me that got me sent here. Brother Christian would be in the exact same position, right? Getting everything at the cost of torturing two others —which is really nothing like the Jesus he worships. And so would you, Sean. Winning the game and having all the numbers play out exactly like your notecards say they will would mean selling out a guy you've fallen for. You know, this whole hunt for the necklace was the real torture all along. But that's over now. So I say—I say we take her down.

Teresa laughs.

TERESA. Take me down, huh?

MELISSA. I didn't trust you from the get-go. You've been lying about something and I think all of this was a trap.

Sean picks up his notecards and flips through them.

SEAN. Wait—there was no point to any of this!

MELISSA. No. There really wasn't.

SEAN. Taking the Heaven offer was a dominated strategy. How did I not see that? It was right in front of me. You broke the game.

EVAN. So . . . there's no chance? No chance I can go to Heaven? We're stuck here?

MELISSA. Yes. But look: we get the chance to start over and change the story. No devil to get in the way. Just us.

TERESA. Oh boy. And how do you plan to do that?

MELISSA. On the first day, you told us exactly how this thing works—

Melissa puts on the talisman and concentrates. The lights in the room flash red and we hear the sound of a swelling, violent thunderstorm.

MELISSA. I'm going to manifest all the powers of Hell with this necklace thing—to destroy you!

The lights return to normal. The violent storm stops. Absolutely nothing has happened. Melissa concentrates again. The lights in the room once again flash red and we hear the sound of a swelling, violent thunderstorm.

MELISSA. To destroy you!

The lights return to normal. The violent storm stops. Absolutely nothing has happened.

TERESA. *(Play-acting.)* Ah! Stop!! I'm melting! *(Cackles.)* What else you got?

MELISSA. Well—if I can't destroy you with this ... I can destroy *it!*

Melissa throws the talisman on the floor and stomps on it. It shatters into pieces. Teresa gasps, genuinely caught off-guard for the first time in this entire experience. Evan and Sean are confused and concerned. Teresa drops to the floor, looking at the talisman pieces and regains her composure. She stands up and then looks at Melissa, Sean, and Evan. Teresa laughs.

TERESA. Well. Well-well-well. Checkmate.

MELISSA. Guys! Charge!! Fight!!

Melissa charges at Teresa. Teresa stops her gently.

TERESA. No—Melissa—checkmate. You got me. I have no moves left.

A beat. Melissa, Sean, and Evan hang in shell-shock confusion for a moment.

TERESA. *(Laughs.)* Which is just as well, since I think enough work has been done. So I'm calling game right here. You each were a little right, and you each were a lot wrong. I lied. My powers don't come from a talisman—I've been operating at full power this whole time. Like that light show just now?

Teresa snaps her fingers. The lights in the room flash red and we hear the sound of a swelling, violent thunderstorm. Teresa snaps her fingers again. The lights return to normal. The violent storm stops.

TERESA. I mean, come on. What would a demon even do with a necklace?

SEAN. Oh my god, this is hilarious.

MELISSA. So—what did I just smash?

TERESA. Oh, who knows? I bought that thing on sale at an

Anthropologie years ago. I was undercover on Earth for a while after shoulder duty. Influenced a couple US elections, actually. Enough about me—there were two lies. It's sort of a good news, bad news kinda thing. Bad news is, talisman or not, I have no way of getting you into Heaven from here.

EVAN. What? Are you serious?

MELISSA. What could possibly be the good news?

TERESA. The good news is I lied about something else. This isn't Hell.

EVAN. You mean—oh my God, I knew it—this is Heaven, where I belonged all along!

TERESA. No—oh, God no.

MELISSA. What kind of sick joke is this?

TERESA. Not a joke. What you've experienced in Brimstone Hall, Room 664 has been very, very real.

SEAN. Oh! This is Purgatory. We talked about it all the time in Catholic school. Uh—so I guess the scenario here, then, is we have to spend however long we need with people who are uniquely good for making us better and eventually go to Heaven. I actually really easily see how that's the case here. That'll be a fun game to crack—

TERESA. I'd actually say you're right, Sean.

SEAN. I usually am.

TERESA. You're all about to leave this room. You'll wake up in different places—familiar places. But I have genuinely no idea where you'll go after that. I'm kinda-sorta actually really low in the rankdown of the heavenly host.

SEAN. Wait—I—what? That doesn't sound like anything I just said. Explain yourself, my brain's turning into shredded beef.

TERESA. Here's what I do know: in a moment you're going to have a very important decision to make. If you've not been paying attention, something eternally bad will happen. Each of you—no exceptions—had a very good reason to be here. Goodbye.

EVAN. What?

TERESA. Goodbye.

Teresa snaps her fingers.

Chapter Nine: White Wine

Act 2, Scene 11

BRIMSTONE HALL, *Room 664, moments later. Teresa sits on the desk alone at center stage in a radiant white dress, with a bottle of white wine and a wine glass handy. Teresa pours herself a glass of wine and sips intermittently.*

TERESA. I think that went all right, wouldn't you say? Really wasn't expecting her to destroy the thing, but—that's okay. It was a gaudy necklace anyway. I've had so much fun since my promotion. I got this idea years ago, when I'd be up on some poor dude's shoulder with the demon Alastor on the other side. Good times, good times. Your guardian angel would never. Anyway! Everyone's insufferable when they're nineteen, aren't they? Some people, you got to lie to a little if they're ever going to do better. There's just something about telling people they died that makes them take you seriously. I don't get it, but it really does seem to work. Seriously, what's so special about dying? For people to realize they need to do better, because this ain't it?

In a corner of the stage, we return to the South-Central Lancaster County Fair. Sean and Adam enter.

ADAM. Yo. I'd be really impressed to see someone finish. Man, they'd be my hero.

SEAN. I'd do it. I'll be your hero.

ADAM. Wait. Really? Not a bluff? Dude . . . what are the odds?

Sean looks at Adam, giving him a flirty, confident smile—complete with an eyebrow raise. He turns to face where Danni would be.

DANNI. *(Offstage.)* . . . and it's all piled on top of Grandma Worley's signature Black-Bottom Hazelnut Pie—a family recipe since 1937!

SEAN. Ah, man. No way, dude. It has hazelnuts. *(Smiles, playful.)* So what are the odds that you go win that woodpecker yourself?

ADAM. Sean.

SEAN. Adam.

Adam and Sean exit. We return focus to Teresa sitting on the desk.

TERESA. I don't know. I really don't know. No one's told me what happens after people die. I don't have a clue. Hell, I don't even know if God is a man or a woman. But maybe that's the fear—no, not God being a woman. It's the not knowing. Not having that firsthand proof of what will actually matter when you watch your soul get weighed. But you know what's funny, I don't think Hell is a place people go when they die. But it's real.

In another corner of the stage, we return to the roof of Andrew Tsui's apartment building. Melissa and Andrew enter.

KRISTA. *(Offstage.)* It's so important that young women understand that building themselves up doesn't mean tearing anyone else down—other women, men, anyone outside the binary. Equality and progress literally can't happen on systemic levels if we say all the right things but don't mean them, wouldn't you say?

ANDREW. *(To Melissa.)* Everything okay?

MELISSA. Yep! I'm just—hey, what's your job title? At the bank?

Andrew laughs.

ANDREW. Wait, are you serious?

MELISSA. Yeah, my friend asked me earlier and I just—totally blanked.

ANDREW. I'm a *hedge* fund manager at an investment bank. Basically what I do is help people bet against the stock market—

MELISSA. Oh! *That's* what you do! Sorry, Krista—yes, absolutely, I agree. I'd actually love to read that paper—

Melissa and Andrew exit. We return focus to Teresa who is still sitting on the desk, nursing her glass of white wine.

TERESA. I did a pretty good job building this torture chamber, if I do say so—two beds, two desks, three people. Classic. But it's nothing compared to what people can build for themselves, when someday, if they're sentenced to Hell —it's little more than a formality.

Teresa gets up from the desk to look at the photos on the wall.

TERESA. Melissa Jones. Sean Liu. Evan Daigle. One of the fun things about being human is that part of who you are is how you suck. Everyone's got this specific, tailored way that they can make the rest of the world miserable. What's that one book say? *Everyone poops.*

Teresa removes the "Abandon All Hoop" banner from the wall.

TERESA. Some will rush to hang their sign for the world to see before they get a chance to proofread. That typo. That damn typo. Well, sometimes you're lucky enough to see what you did and just lean in where you went wrong—make something better out of it. That doesn't work all the time— but it works out more than you'd think it would. This ended up being perfect, drove them all insane.

Teresa sets the banner down. In another corner of the stage, we return to the sidewalk next to a busy street on the campus of Freedom University. Evan and Rachel enter.

RACHEL. I . . . it really just feels like I'm using you.

EVAN. That's how the world dates. But as Christians, we're preparing for marriage.

RACHEL. No—Evan. I don't think I could marry you. That's the point.

A beat.

RACHEL. I've been coming to terms realizing—I—I like girls. Maybe also guys. I—I really, uh—if I look back on certain people . . . and feelings I've felt that were more than friendship . . . I know I've fallen for women before. And when I think about how desperately you want me—I've tried to get there, Evan. I could list out all these reasons why I should find you attractive . . . but . . . it's not fair. It's not fair for you to keep—

Rachel trails off as she tries to find an eloquent thought. She frustratedly blurts out:

RACHEL. Evan, I'm bi. Or gay. Maybe. I don't know.

Silence. Evan gathers his thoughts.

EVAN. I'm only saying this because I love you . . . I'm sorry. I really do like you.

RACHEL. This—it's all really new to me. I hope we can still be friends.

EVAN. (*Nods, slowly.*) Yeah. Maybe we can.

Evan and Rachel smile back and forth at each other. We hear a bus drive by. Evan and Rachel exit. We end with Teresa sitting back down on the desk as she pours another glass of wine.

TERESA. A soul is built or destroyed piece by piece. Moment by moment. If you can still find a moment that you're willing to take a good, hard look at what your life is building—you never need to abandon all hope.

Teresa finishes the wine in her glass.

THE END.

Acknowledgments

Thank you first and foremost to my editor, Kimberly Macasevich, and my publicist, Regina Menninger, for the incredible work you've done to help me get *Abandon All Hope* ready to make its second debut—the real one—into readers' hands in print. It's been quite a journey and I'm forever grateful I had the two of you with me through it all.

Thank you to my dad, Jim Fenton, for being by my side through every step of the journey with *Abandon All Hope*—from being the very first person to read the first draft and calling me out on the fact that I hadn't yet told the story I wanted to tell, through the audiobook version of the first edition, to wherever exactly it is we've landed now. It's been quite a learning journey walking through the publishing industry with you. Thank you for being along with me as I try new things and always encouraging me to learn from my mistakes.

Thank you to my mom, Beth Fenton, for the daily walks we took while I was drafting the first and second iterations of *Abandon All Hope* and letting me often monopolize that time by talking through my plot and character developments out loud. I believe it takes a very special type of person to be married to one author and mother of another—and you are doing an exceptional job.

Thank you to my dear friend, Kylie Marble, for bringing your lived perspective to the table as I got Rachel's hard-hitting lines in Evan's death scene where they needed to be. I'm so grateful for our bond from Christian college and how it's evolved since.

Thank you to Tony Gapastione and BraveMaker Media for believing in *Abandon All Hope* to give it its very first platform and thank you to Avery Kellington, Geoffrey Ko, Natalia Dominguez, and Krystina Jackson for each of your early portrayals of these characters—Avery and Krystina have each portrayed TERESA, Natalia portrayed MELISSA, and Geoffrey portrayed SEAN. It was in hearing your voices give life to these rich stories that I learned beyond a shadow of a doubt this one was a story worth sharing with the masses.

Thank you to each and every one of my early readers who inspired me to keep going and reach higher—too many to list here, but ones especially jumping to mind include Walter Roper, Jen Lowry, Ana Neimus, Lillah Lawson, Jenna Kraft, Cheryl King, Jamie Hitt, Katie Gilgour, Frances McCoy, and Brad Hawkins.

Thank you to Debbie Rodgers and Kim Spradlin Wolfe for helping me as I neared publication of the first edition to reframe my lived experience into a win and not abandon all hope in 2020.

And finally, thank you to another important teacher in my life, Dr. Emily Langan, for blowing my mind with Standpoint Theory all those years ago in your Gender & Communication lectures. I've never thought about gender, race, class, or sexuality the same way since.

About the Author

Peter Fenton's work has appeared in or is forthcoming from Dadley Productions, Heuer Publishing, OurBible App, and Q Christian Fellowship among others. Peter is an adventurous multi-genre author and screenwriter drawn to creating clever and self-aware works stimulating critical thought and laughter. He wrote and produced the profitable world premiere of his holiday satire *See Amid the Winter Snow* (2019), as well as his dark spiritual comedy, *Abandon All Hope* (2020), a co-production with BraveMaker Media. Peter served as the President and Director of Jukebox Theatre at Wheaton College and is an alumnus of the postgraduate apprenticeship program at Walnut Street Theatre in Philadelphia. As an up-and-coming screenwriter and playwright, Peter is a member of the Dramatists Guild of America.

You can connect with Peter on his website at www.byPeterFenton.com or follow him on Twitter and Instagram @peterfent!

YOUR NEXT READ

First Circle
by Jim Fenton

Follow the faith and character journeys of six individuals connected to a pugnacious, retired professor battling cancer who are receiving messages crafted by a hand from afar. This magical realism novel from debut author Jim Fenton is a thrilling tale with charming prose!

Shakespeare in The Parking Lot
by Peter Fenton

This collection of three family-friendly adventure comedies traverses a fairy tale kingdom, a mythical Irish city, and a 21st Century take on Santa Claus' North Pole! These three plays are lighthearted fun and aren't taking themselves too seriously . . . it's Shakespeare in the parking lot!